MW00856135

Also by Joan Frank

JUNIPER STREET: A NOVEL

JOAN FRANK

C&R Press
Conscious & Responsible
Winston-Salem, NC

All Rights Reserved

Printed in the United States of America

First Edition
1 2 3 4 5 6 7 8 9

Selections of up to two pages may be reproduced without permission. To reproduce more than two pages of any one portion of this book, write to C&R Press publishers John Gosslee and Andrew Ibis.

Cover art by John Willis

Copyright ©2022 Joan Frank
ISBN 978-1-949540-34-5
LCCN 2022942168

C&R Press
Conscious & Responsible
crpress.org

For special discounted bulk purchases, please contact:
C&R Press sales@crpress.org
Contact info@crpress.org to book events, readings and author signings.

*For T.G. and extended family. For J.M.,
who's cared so long, so deeply.*

Above all and always, for Mary.

Oh, remember them kindly in their time of trouble; and in the hour of their taking away.

— James Agee, "Knoxville, Summer of 1915"

JUNIPER STREET

1

Tommy's Letter

Dear —,

I hope you'll remember me: Tom Hamlin from Juniper Street. I saw your article in the San Francisco magazine, and have been meaning to write ever since.

It was good realizing it was actually you, after reading your piece about memory. I'd love to get together and talk old times. So much has changed since the days on Juniper Street.

Mom, Dad, and Mary are dead. My sister Lucy and brother Reeve are fine. I've lived the last 20 years in ——.

Please give me a call or drop a note, and we can meet each other and talk.

I miss people from my past.

Yours,

Tom Hamlin

I fished the envelope from the pile at the bottom of my damp, evil-smelling stairwell. *Tommy Hamlin*—return address, some unheard-of Nevada town. Fumbled to rip it open.

Stood with it, staring.

Sacramento Summer

A sick-bright Polaroid: heavy heat clamped over the city, stretched across suburbs. Vast, shimmering, still. Tangles of freeways fed in and out like hospital tubing, into a downtown whose skyline jutted cylindrical from that great dusty flatland—cars' and trucks' foul exhalations so clotted by heat that, with no wind to sweep it away, a dim brown screen covered land and sky. Creeks dried up. Leaves went gray or hardened where they hung. Grass yellowed; houses were baked clay.

We dashed from house to car on Juniper Street because the heat closed fast around you, a kind of paste. It seeped into your eyes. Your skin began to smart; your heart to thrum; beads of moisture swam in all your creases and over your scalp. Your lungs panicked, and only in the safety of an air-conditioned room could they release the sigh of close-call, expand again with the next inhale.

The fabled Central Valley heat bore down harder as day advanced; by evening it had cooked streets and buildings, wafting from them in waves all night. The wind—if it came—blew hot, and to gaze out a window and see leaves riffling on branches was not to be fooled. Skin stung after you came indoors, sometimes blotched red. We drank gallons of chilled diet soda at my house in those years, ate cantaloupe, played Parcheesi, read library books. We stared out at the glare of day pressing down on trees, buildings, earth.

In remembering Mary, the images are often set against this heat—a stillness that seemed to stop time, to paralyze both past and future as if all movement, ever after, had been canceled. Yet move we did—the human given, maybe the only one while we live. Events did enter, like creeping armies, fanning out and sweeping forward everyone's course. Did we ourselves set all the stories in motion, or did they simply drop onto us, like space debris?

Isn't that what's always asked when we pause to consider our pasts?

When I held in my hands that note from Tommy Hamlin all those years ago—at least thirty years after knowing Mary—I told myself I wanted to know what had happened.

But for reasons still not clear, I let Tommy's note float among my effects. A simple, ruled yellow 4-by 8-inch sheaf torn from a drugstore scratchpad, printed neatly in black ballpoint pen. It spilled from my papers, took temporary shelter in this file or that.

One day it spilled into view again.

Houses

My father brought us to the house on Juniper Street, in the new suburb of the college where he would begin teaching, following my mother's sudden death. We had left Phoenix almost at once. It was the only choice; my father had already signed his teaching contract and now—on the surface of things—it appeared he could make a fresh start for us. My little sister and I were still kids, dazed, disoriented. He remarried soon after: a woman who looked like the long-ago actress Jane Wyman. She wore makeup and perfume; dressed in form-fitting knit ensembles that required dry cleaning. We had no initial reason to object to our stepmother, but we had no clarity about anything at all then, nor for a very long time to come. What I remember wanting before anything else—wishing here I could report something braver, or more original—was to be thought normal. To blend in, seen as unremarkable, living a normal life. Mute, furled tightly, I wanted fiercely, beyond all else, to feel like nothing had happened—to impress that upon others. *Nothing to see here.*

Perhaps I simply wanted not to feel.

We were told our mother had died of a heart attack in her sleep. I walked around staring at the ground, trying to understand that sequence.

Sleep: then, nothing. Blackness giving over to eternal blackness. Dreams, perhaps, cutting to a blank screen. No thing.

Somewhere in that blurry transit to a new city, our father visited the admissions offices of the local elementary and middle schools to explain why my sister and I had to enroll late. How I remember this, I don't know. How those conversations may have played out, I can only wonder. But I can still see my father's face during those days: gray, drawn, purposive. He looked much older than his years (I now grasp). He would, as it turns out, have only thirteen more years to live. But then—fogged, almost catatonic—I had no sense of any other way for a father to look. I adored him. He would have been forty-one.

At first only the three of us, my father and sister and me, lived in an old apartment my father had hastily rented, set back from Winding Way in the shadows of a conifer woods, shabby and chilly inside, stained wallpaper smelling of mildew. (These are the particulars that never leave you, that carry a sickening weight.) It was furnished like one of those motels in a 50s postcard: checked oilcloth on the kitchen table, ridged-chenille bedspreads, peeling paint, diaphanous nylon limp over windows. My father slept on the couch, giving my sister and me the single, tiny bedroom—we little girls each, I think, had a cot-sized bed. A clock-radio sat on the kitchen table. For some reason I felt fiercely that this radio should be kept tuned at all times to the local easy listening station, convinced that such music would soothe us, my father, sister, and me—the clutch of us like some mortally wounded animal, staggering about on three legs.

This was before my new stepmother flew over to join us. Arrangements, unbeknownst to my sister and me, had been made—quite rapidly, thinking back on it. My dad had rented a plush suburban house for when she arrived: it boasted a sunken living room, very modish for the time. I can't recall the activities of moving in, but it seemed to happen fast—perhaps because we owned so little. An intense sexual fug quickly filled that house: that I do clearly recall. My father and stepmother drank, exchanged soulful glances, reclined in easy chairs aligned beside each other; they held hands between the chairs while Tony Bennett and Lotte Lenya sang on the stereo. This scene and its soundtrack, when I came upon it by chance (from behind them, so they never saw me), made me queasy. Yet part of me assumed this was what adults did when they fell in love—and my father, I told myself, deserved some happiness.

Then our dad bought the house on Juniper Street, part of a new suburban tract near the college—a futuristic village; each home a variant of the same low, simplified A-lines, at that time considered bold and avant-garde. Daringly, some used colored gravel for front yards instead of grass. The tract was laid out on cleared acres once lumpy with scrub, still surrounded by low-growing oaks, tufts of grass, wild lilies, daffodils. A halfhearted creek crossed the suburb's borders; pocked here and there by rough gaps, odd parcels of property where a few shambly old houses still stood—their owners too stubborn to sell—guarded by a twisted oak or two.

It was those old houses that I always wanted to know.

Down the street, not yet known to me, was Mary's.

Ghosts

In those years, when you drove through certain parts of old Sacramento, along the outskirts by the river, where people you never saw dwelt in trailers and cabins amid junk strewn like a trail—stripped cars, decomposing rowboats, dogs, tents, half-buried toys, deflated basketballs—you'd occasionally come upon these lone, tall ghosts.

Skinny, splintering, listing old Victorians, somebody's once-earnest notion of a homestead—that was the part that punched me, the *earnest* part. Often these marked the patch of land at the end of a cul-de-sac, or rose gaunt and shimmery like a mirage at some distance from the freeway, slightly slumped, by itself in the middle of an alfalfa field. A lonely sentry. They looked forgotten, those decrepit frameworks, but maybe someone still lived there. There was never time to look long enough, growing up—still less time as a young adult, when I drove brooding to the Sierras to visit my by-then-grown-and-married sister. Always, during those years, I flinched to glimpse these tall structures, their skull faces. They seemed to accuse me. Of what? Being born so much later? Never giving them enough attention, or never the right kind of attention? How I wished I could slip through their filthy, cobwebby windows and poke at whatever dwelt inside: bones, liquor bottles, medicine bottles, papers covered with water-stained writing, rags, crockery, rusty cans. It nauseated and titillated and made me sleepy all at once, the way old sepia photos did—a kind of stricken, druggy arousal. Rust-hued people in high-collared dresses and bowler hats facing the camera—unreadable yet stoic, quiet and blank as dying animals. Like the old houses, they, too, accused.

You wanted to know. You didn't want to know.

What was their heyday, these collapsing masses of splintered wood once nailed together with such hard resolve? What had people done and said in there? How had their voices sounded when they spoke; what words had they used? What had they dreamed? Walls buckling, wizened, last chips of paint whipped off by round upon round of seasons; weeds and tree-stumps and what had been yards, lumped, dank, woolly. Boxlike extensions had at some point been tacked onto main structures, perhaps with the births of children. Now these sections sagged drunkenly: jutting eaves, porches, narrow rooms stuck out in odd directions like dividing cells.

The Hamlins lived at the end of Juniper Street in one such druid, dug into a raised fold of wooded land which, though only a few steps from my own sleek suburb, abruptly dropped the visitor out of present time. The house must first have stood in the center of raw woods, before Mary and I were born. No question that Faith and Clive Hamlin had kept animals when they set up there as young marrieds—grown children of immigrants fled west during the 40s, like so many others, for the imagined Eden. Of course they'd need animals. Certainly they'd have kept goats and chickens. Maybe a pig, a cow. Could those days and years have added up, then or ever, to what they themselves would have called a good life? (Did anyone stop, in the midst of their strivings, to reckon such a thing?) You could still spot remnants of partitioned-off pens: places in the rumpled yard where the earth had once been tilled and piled for plots, vegetables, flowers, manure, or trampled and tamped by long-gone animals; a caved-in hutch. There was a separate, ancient garage—a sinking bungalow, crude and homely as a child's drawing, shaped to cover what used to be called a Tin Lizzie—boards and beams decomposing where they merged with earth, exactly the near-black color of the plant-matter reclaiming them. Their rickety remains sheltered piles of old tools and pots—a museum of decay: baby-carriage wheels, splayed umbrella ribs, stained lampshades, moldy pillows, rust-crusted bicycle chains, shredded tires, a flour sifter, coffee cans, crumbling boxes of papers, collapsed pup tents, flattened Army issue water rafts, dust-coated rolls of plastic sheeting, canvas, tarpaper, half-unscrolled posters whose designs had long ago washed out. Outside, against the mossy apex of the roof, a nail secured one end of a makeshift clothesline; the other end was tied to a tree. The garage stayed dark inside, smelling of machine oil and soil and rotting cardboard and moist grass, fat green blades jutting through the rot and wood. House and yard and garage stood far enough back from the street to wear its out-of-time woodsiness like a misty garland. Nothing changed or stirred; the homestead grew older and moldier where it rooted, merging by finite grains with its surroundings year after year.

As if nurtured by this rank, fertile setting, all our stories pushed up and opened.

Juniper Street

The lawn sloped steeply upward from Juniper Street to the Hamlin place, lodged in a sudden hill—a sort of Shangri-La transition. Toward the hill's crest a giant oak so thoroughly draped house and lawn with dense, leaf-thickened limbs, you hardly saw anything except the tree. I walked the gray concrete, past the quiet homes like mine, until just before the road's turn, turning up to the left and almost crouching to hike the rest, steep and tree-hidden. People driving that bend would never suspect a house stood there: you had to already know about it and be looking for it. To get to the door you were forced to duck the oak's lowest branches—and then to dodge the angry gander who guarded the place, Gus. How or when or why the family had acquired him, I never knew. His eyes were sharp, his temper worse, and for a big fellow he was fast. He'd spot the interloper, screech and flap and hiss, aim himself like a spear at the foreigner, cranking along in pursuit at amazing speed, white neck stretched long, cold vengeance in his eye. Lord knew what would happen to any flesh that hard yellow bill might actually grab. I was terrified of Gus—adrenalin prickling behind my knees as I double-timed it up the cement stairs to the front door, where I'd bang frantically with my fist during what seconds of intact rear remained me. And just in that last saving second, whoever opened the door—Faith or one of the kids (father Clive upstairs sick or drunk or sleeping)—would shoo Gus off: *Ah shut up, ya crazy bird.*

Their voices held a disgusted authority the bird seemed to recognize and obey with great reluctance: only then would he pull back his murderous neck, flap a couple of furious flaps and stalk off, cursing bitterly.

I remember stepping into the Hamlins' small, crowded living room—more passageway than room. Directly across from the front door sat a couch covered by an old Indian blanket; at the right a bookcase below a circular window like a ship's porthole. (These objects, and every scrap of furniture throughout the

Hamlin house, were so old and worn that any color had long ago bled from them, resulting in the uniform hue, for every surface, of dull brown.) Between sofa and bookcase, a small, arched door to a tiny coat closet, like something cut from gingerbread. Behind the sofa a steep staircase led to the bedrooms—the sort of boxy, secret-passage staircase from days of old clapboard mansions and fairy tales. Any child might instantly assume they were magical. But I would never venture up those stairs unless Mary preceded me: the decrepit, angry Clive dwelt up there, and I was afraid of Clive. No one ever said it, but I knew Clive was sick (with what, nobody said), and drunk, and sort of insane—partly, I guessed, alcohol glued those facts together in ways not fully understandable, at least not yet.

Toward the kitchen, on the left, stood a dilapidated upright piano, which still sounded good when Faith Hamlin, the family's hard-put-upon matriarch, sat down to it. What would Faithie play? Scott Joplin rags. *Maple Leaf* was one. Faith banged it out with determination, as if she were arguing with someone. But sometimes big brother Reeve (too handsome for words) would take a few minutes from whatever urgency he was pursuing (Painting? Sculpting? Car repair? Woodworking? Girls?) to seat his shapely hulk before the black-painted upright. Half-smiling into nothingness, he'd bend over his large, oil-and-paint-stained hands, and commence one of the *Goldbergs*, or Rachmaninoff's *Variations on a Theme of Paganini*. He'd hum the melody while he played, out his nostrils.

It gave me shivers.

2

Vista Bonita Road

Life was cleaved in two after our mother died: everything that had happened until then made one world, and everything that came after, another.

I could not, ever again, say the words *Mother* or *Mom* or *Mommy* or *Mama*.

I couldn't utter any version of them.

I can't say them now.

I can only say *my mother* or *our mother* or, more rarely, *my mom*— distanced by the specifying *my* or *our*, its courteous, even clinical formality. Much later I would refer to her by her darkly beautiful name, *Marion*. The name's music embodied her to me; still does. It also let me feel I was referring to her from an almost sororal understanding: that of the adult I became.

But for many years it was always grindingly difficult to utter the word *died*, that single, slicing syllable. Decapitating whoosh-thud. Animal-dumb. *Died*.

After a time, though, I made myself say it. I said it to people deliberately, to test its shock.

The pattern proved so predictable it cast a spell that, morbidly, seduced me. (It made me understand, much later, how door-to-door salespeople, or missionaries, refined their manipulations.)

Pleasant preliminaries: How-d'you do. Followed by the inevitable. Where're you from?

Phoenix. Then our mother died, and we moved here.

———.

———.

Died. Died. Died.

As if I'd produced a small, gleaming knife and plunged it double-quick in-out of my listener's chest. Zip-zap.

Instantly faces dropped or rearranged: scared, reverent, sad. Always immediate, always visible. I watched faces register various confusions, while the owners of the faces also searched—gazing through, above, around me—for what they could possibly say next. Because she or he, let's remember, was talking to a child.

Why did I do it? Part of me—baffling even while it gripped me—was fascinated by the reliable mechanism of the sequence, the purring clock of it, almost soothing for its sturdy regularity. Another part of me, writhing and wretched, only wanted to stop existing, become invisible, leave no trace.

Two halves of existence, then: the Beginning, and What Came Next. Under those monikers stood the sub-territories: Marion Alive and Marion No Longer. The former country already fading—rather, being veiled by the fine-grained scrim of time, trading concrete memory for gas-lit dreams.

In that country—the Phoenix part—we lived on Vista Bonita Road, unpaved for the first years, in a brand-new little post-war development of simple, matchbox houses. Ours cost ten thousand dollars, my dad once told me, which then seemed a phenomenal amount. He and Marion must have moved into it just before I was born.

At first, I am guessing, things were beautiful.

Most first things are beautiful, are they not?

Hamlin House

All the Hamlin kids were double-take striking. It filled me with wonder. But especially Reeve, the oldest—nearly twenty—before he went off to live in Berkeley. Reeve was, for me, a movie star. I could hardly bear to look at him. Tall and broad-chested like Superman, soft brown hair parted on the side, tan skin like chocolate milk, mocking light-blue eyes. He said little, but his smile held a knowingness that nearly blinded me. I was neither girl nor woman then—fourteen, that terrible, blobby, sprouting age—and felt homely and sexless around Reeve, too wretched even to meet the gaze of this grown and clever, mischievous god, this stunning big brother of my friend. He seemed to understand things that (to him) were deliciously funny— things just offstage of my own awareness that I was too naïve to notice, let alone comprehend. When he smiled at me—though I know he meant no meanness—it was as though he were laughing at a cartoon painted unbeknownst to me on my forehead. Though I never saw the women Reeve dated, I assumed they were goddesses. They had to be; had to own a quality of femininity I could never dream of possessing, the kind you saw in magazines—sylph-slim, delicate wrists, tiny pert noses, silken hair and skin—like exquisite Tuptim, who made me cry when she sang *We Kiss in the Shadow*. Catlike, goddess eyes. In those days I still pretty much thought people were meant to find their perfect, romantic matches in beauty and temperament. Once this happened, I assumed, the divine pair flew up to heaven entwined like doves, to stand together on the balcony of their cloud-castle sunset kingdom (pink, orange, mango) and beam down at their cheering subjects, waving like kindly royals. Luckily for me, Mary never seemed to notice my choked awe around Reeve, so I was spared her teasing (though I think Mary was then too deeply immersed in her own dreams to consider anything else).

I tried not to think about how goofy I must appear, compared with Reeve's goddesses.

I tried to avoid running into him.

Animals pervaded the Hamlin camp, constant as the food on their stove. With the children's bright fancies came the goldfish and guppies, parakeets and canaries, guinea pigs and hamsters and white rats and once, a big box tortoise making slow tours out in the yard. These took their turns being treasured, then lost or run over, or perishing of some unknown illness or predator. Varmit was the name of a kitten I remember from early visits, a skinny bug-eyed calico that probably had tapeworms and heaven knew what else, scrambling and darting in frenzies. (I wrote a poem for the Hamlins, honoring their chaos by itemizing it—how I wish I'd somehow kept this poem—its last line, I remember, was *Varmit on the stair.*) When I arrived, I would toy with the maddened creature, plunk a few keys on the piano (I knew the beginning of *Für Elise* and also that dutiful, singsong Bach piece everyone can play or hum the beginning of). But by force of psychic law, I always drifted into the kitchen—where everyone convened and everything happened, and where there were sights and smells to make saliva well up in your cheeks.

Even the Hamlins' leftovers seemed wondrous.

All their food thrilled me. Real, unapologetic food. The dense, rich, truck-driver kind advertised by family restaurants and casinos, the kind people with no second thoughts about eating demanded and devoured. It wasn't that I was not fed at home, but my parents' relationship to food was complicated, furtive, embattled. My stepmother was grim and controlling about what we ate. She kept a special off-limits drawer in the refrigerator for her own expensive delicacies; I remember looking with longing at her untouchable Havarti cheese in that drawer, and once in a while I stole a slice, I'm sure, trying to make it look unnoticeable. Her attitude toward cooking for us was military—that of churning out quantity grimly, as if for a halfway house or orphanage. *Cheap mass* was the driving creed. She made big skillets of fried rice, bought canned green beans and stewed tomatoes by the case. For us girls she bought chicken backs on sale in bulk, which she'd broil unadorned on a cookie sheet in the oven. You had to eat a lot of chicken backs, working the two shallow strips of flesh from the bone, to finally feel as if you'd eaten something. She and my father were always trying to lose weight, but their appetites were furious, as if compensating for so much else—so their eating happened in sudden surges. She wolfed cheese and crackers at speed, in a kind of anger. My father mashed raw ground beef in a bowl with a raw egg, salt, pepper, and a dash of worcestershire. He called the oily, blood-smelling result steak tartare, and gulped it down.

By contrast, the brazen richness of the Hamlin menu dumbfounded me. Faith always kept a heavy stew going, chicken or pork or beef, or a pot of thick dark chili or split peas with ham hocks, together with pans of moist cornbread—more like sweet corn-cake. Or she'd hand forth a platter stacked with fried chicken, golden and crisp, together with a vat of fluffy mashed potatoes and spicy coleslaw. Or she'd haul from the oven a deeper pan of marinara-drenched lasagna, or enchiladas swimming in melted cheese. Or she had just that moment turned out a tower of puffy pancakes or waffles, shoving the plated pile toward you followed by (second shove) a bowl of soft butter, with bottles of warmed maple and blackberry and blueberry syrup. Always, along the countertops, we found canisters of chewy cookies, sheets of brownies or Irish soda bread, bowls of cold fruit I'd never tasted before, kumquats, gooseberries, cherimoya—once you tasted you could not stop—persimmons, pomegranates, fat purple figs. Fluffy hot biscuits, meat loaf, mashed potatoes and gravy: lumberjack food that soothed and warmed and stupefied. It would stop my heart to consume that stuff now. You rinsed it all down with iced tea into which a good half-cup of sugar had been stirred. Afterward you felt a bit stunned, but also (we were kids) as if you could go for miles, which we girls proceeded to do. The entire family, though they ate with relish, remained skinny as scarecrows. The heavenly food seemed another form of Faith's loaves-and-fishes magic, because the Hamlins never, never had money. I don't know how Faith managed it. They must have received Social Security; probably some sort of government pension, what with Clive retired and sick. Maybe food stamps. But how they fed four children and whatever other needy creature tumbled through—I couldn't figure. I wouldn't learn until later that the family's want ran deep and sharp; that it was part of their ultimate undoing.

For more years than I am willing to name, this story has hung over me—haunting, hounding. I tell it at last from the strangely freeing vantage of age—looking back with the kind of sad settledness that only time can allow. Once, the body's urge was to leap to intervene. Now it can only witness.

I warn you: the memory won't finally sweeten out like a piece of ironed ribbon.

I tell it to loosen its grip.

How It Was

I listened to my mother and father fighting after I went to bed, in the little Phoenix house.

My younger sister, only eight, must have slept soundly. At ten, I carried—gravely—an elder sibling's sense of duty; it fell to me automatically to shepherd the two of us, to guard, protect, navigate for us both. Unforgettable is the white light that rimmed the blacked-out bedroom door, seeming to frame some other dimension: I knew the light had traveled like a river down the hall from the living room, mapping the different world of the house at night, especially when my parents ranted at each other. In our tiny bedroom the darkness felt gentle. I have always believed that the house itself felt very sorry for what was happening inside it—for what would happen—so quiet, except for the loving murmur of the evaporative cooler, it let me hear their raised voices.

I lay on my back with my eyes open, listening. I could not make out the words, could not grasp the conflict's nature, could not imagine any reason for it except somehow (a child's mind grapples for sense) either a clash of personalities, or—far likelier to me—something I had done. The sound of their voices—alternating tones, his exasperation, her imploring—hurt my stomach.

Dreadful silences hovered in a terrible, weighted way, between the back-and-forth sounds. These hurt almost worse.

They thought we little girls were sleeping.

At my core, I feared their ordeal, their battle, was my fault. Something I had said or done or been, some irreparable bad thing in me, made them fight.

Maybe it was the fact that I loved him better.

Themselves

The four, in order of their births, were Reeve, Mary, Tommy, and Lucy. All were wildly beautiful. All understood the score—as often happens in large families where one or both parents have drunk themselves into permanent stupors (too many children, too much need, crises swirling in mad confinement like snow-globe flakes). The Hamlin children saw what they had been born into: a kind of *laissez-faire* anarchy. Children size up their straits like animals, and generally—also like animals—act instinctively to save themselves. From the start, the Hamlin kids had to figure things out, make their own ways, fight for space or favor or things. All came late in the marriage—by my then-standards, Faith and Clive were already alarmingly old. They had compounded that effect by having lived hard. Clyde looked to be in his late seventies, Faithie in her late sixties when I knew them. Yet I now know they were both in fact at least a decade younger. They behaved like cartoons of old folks—addled, rickety, puttering and gabbling in witless, chaotic monologues of complaint. Faith commandeered the downstairs; we tried to avoid her but that was difficult, since she tended to hover where most of the action took place: the kitchen. I guessed that since she'd made the food she felt entitled to watch it be eaten—more sadly, to be near someone to talk to. Often we'd walk away while she was still nattering on like a disgruntled duck. *And then I SAID the price was twenty-nine cents a POUND but they never LISTENED and they said forty-ONE and tell me WHERE we were supposed to find OUT and HOW could you be EXPECTED now I ASK YOU.* Faith's thoughts would dribble out and out and out, each puddling into the next like watery whey, producing a helpless, whiny singsong like Olive Oyl's that faded and resumed for no reason. I wanted Mary to get us away from this display as fast as possible; it made my insides twist up with embarrassment and a kind of hapless shame for everybody in the room. I figured it kept on that way much of the day and night, if we'd been around to listen.

By contrast, none of the Hamlin kids, as far as I could see, ever felt any need to defend or explain the theater of it all; the way Faith and Clive shambled and sweated and cursed and fumbled through the house—through their lives. None of the four seemed troubled or embarrassed. They just stepped around their whingeing parents as they might a vaguely annoying dog or cat. This was practical. For the kids the house was a staging area; survival demanded moving in the straightest line toward your desire. There wasn't room for subterfuge. Reeve and Mary and Tommy and Lucy were not cold or cruel or thoughtless. They were just steady-at-the-helm of their own wheelhouses, as many children learn to be. At the same time, never once did I see any of the kids express affection for their parents. Affection, I see now, had no usefulness there: if ever it once had, that period was of a time long past. Affection would have squandered energy and possibly left the kids vulnerable but also, I'm bound to say, would have been false. I don't know that they ever felt love, or something they might have been willing to call love, for their parents. That lack—a sort of blank space—has not struck me, then or now, as a sin. When your parents are crazy, you've neither time nor emotional capital to ponder it at length. It's just a given, like air. You act to survive: a habit of daily, low-level triage. To risk vulnerability in a scenario like that would take you down and hold you under. The Hamlin kids handled their parents briskly, in passing. They didn't bother with self-pity, or pity for anybody. Everything was provisional, and could vanish on a dime. Whatever might be available that day—food, cadging a couple of dollars, borrowing the single, barely-functioning car—had to be seized. The kids endured so as to fill immediate needs: meals, a bed, a ride.

It strikes me now that the above can describe, in truth, a timeless tactic by the young everywhere.

So we suffered what could only very loosely pass for talk with Faith, as we ate at her table—a diner-booth, Formica, built next to a picture window. Through it, we looked out to the crumbling garage and weedy garden, the stooping oaks giving way to woods, the clothesline, the massed silver clouds. The setting must have seemed bold when Clive first built it, but it only felt cramped and funky by the time I was walking its warped floorboards. We were children. The world at hand was a dull constant, without history or explanation. The lives and bodies of the elderly, leaking memories and opinions like a faucet not properly shut, seemed almost shockingly irrelevant. It mortified us.

We suffered listening to Faith's mewling in order to stuff ourselves with her food. But the dining booth served also as a gallery for watching family dramas. Reeve and Tommy would bang in from the back, where they were fixing old cars and motorcycles out in the dark garage. Smelling of machine oil, fingernails black, they'd stand there grime-streaked and grinning like crazed RAF pilots just hopped from the cockpit, wiping their hands on rags after returning from some death-cheating mission. Their dark skin and cocoa hair, their flashing eyes—Reeve's skyblue, Tommy's darkest chocolate—made me mute, agog. Yet neither, careless and filthy, ever seemed aware of his thrilling physical impact. At some point little Lucy—maybe seven or eight in those days, sparklingly pretty, self-possessed, eager—would descend the stairs with slow poise like a regal film star, draped in shiny fabrics she hoped resembled princess veils. As a girl she looked like the child-actress Margaret O'Brien. Doubtless she has grown up, like the others, to be a fine-looking woman—surely well past middle-age now. One morning, completing her film-star descent of the stairs, I remember, she declared with satisfied pomp that she had brushed her teeth twice, and planned to do so forevermore.

At unpredictable intervals Clive would stagger downstairs a slow, awful series of clumps and start hobbling around, grunting and growling. Tall, gaunt, silver-haired, hunched and shaky, salt-and-pepper mustache like a cleaning brush, his eyes and eyelids and the tumor-pink satchels beneath his eyes seemed to be melting down, sliding off. You could see, however at least vaguely that once, long long ago, Clive must have been handsome. A Faulkner or a Hammett, with a fedora. Rakish, hard-boiled, Clive must have cut—as would have been said of such types—a suave, commanding figure. Now his voice and veiny hands trembled, his cheeks were pleated, and his eyes watered like an old dog's. His thoughts seemed to take a long time to get to his mouth, emerging in a hoarse slur. He was usually sputtering-angry, enraged with everything. As is the case with most angry alcoholics, the general cause seemed a sort of smeary agglomeration of injustices, a lifetime's deliberate, vague, canny, and multi-pronged thwartings and attacks: volleys of arrows from all directions. In his bathrobe, sliding his slippered feet along in small *shuss-shusses,* shussing his way across the scuffed kitchen linoleum toward the bathroom, carping the whole time at Faith about a range of offenses I could never quite make out; sometimes at the kids, I remember, for being *ungrateful useless bums.* This would set Faith going in her protesting whine as she fussed with cake batter or noodles or boiling eggs—I can see and hear it still, the snowy white light of California day sheening over her frumpled, harassed form (her Einsteinian tufts of gray-white hair) and cluttered surfaces, him continuing his slow locomotion through the rooms, a bitter old clocktower figure marking the hour in transit, muttering and shuffling, head swaying slowly; her own whingeing in counterpoint. They were two dashboard figurines, he and Faith, heads bobbling, eyes dribbling, chanting gibberish in two different keys to no one in particular.

Fascinated, sickened, silent, I'd shrink down in my corner of the dining booth. I had a terror that one of them would catch sight of me and confront me in some sudden, focused wrath, like fire-breath from a dragon—maybe angry that I was eating their food. I had no sense what any of it meant, or how I should behave.

When I think about it now, knowing more, I have let myself wonder: what could have reversed this? Even if a chest filled with money had arrived to their front step that day (vanquishing the damned gander), how might Faith and Clive have set about reviving themselves, remaking themselves back into sensible, functioning beings? Maybe it would have been a matter of hospitalizing them—assuming they'd accept that, which seems unlikely, and assuming a hospital could have restored them. Or maybe it would have meant

parking them in assisted living, had such a facility existed and—
again unlikely—had they consented.

I'm not sure money could have fixed them at that point, they
were so far gone. That makes the trap of their predicament seem
airtight, therefore sadder.

After an eternity, to my unspeakable relief, Clive would limp
and shuffle out of the room. How he got back up the stairs I'll
never know. His punishing inspections seemed to take forever,
and I felt a little bullet of shame in my chest for wishing he would
just disappear. Mary told me he'd once been a newspaper reporter
and photographer for the local newspaper; done fancy things with
fancy people. I conjured, like a silent film, Clive's days as a looker
and player: the full-cut suits, the tall, loping ease, smirky twinkle,
Clark Gable fedora. It was easy to picture him drinking in noisy
downtown bars with other reporters who joked and mugged like
him, a gang of handsome scalawags grabbing trolleys, swinging
from streetlamp poles, wisecracking at women, wry and sly and
funny. Surely there'd have been drunken newsroom parties; surely
he'd worn a lampshade on his head at one or another of them;
surely he'd also worn a pencil behind one ear and written notes
in dark soft lead on little spiral pads kept in his pockets—typed
up those notes with two fingers at a big clattering Underwood,
cigarette pasted to lower lip—squinting at his own dashing, hasty,
masculine print, small capital letters in some abbreviation system
he'd cooked up himself.

Conjuring these sequences, I also remember the early pangs of
a peculiar, creeping awareness. With no words for it and without
anyone else ever saying so, I began to sense that this state-of-
Clive told of a pattern, a certain, fundamental way of things. That
there would never be an adequate response or reward—no chance
for an old man to receive whatever an old man might feel due
him—for having lived boldly, done good work, kept inside the
law, made a family, built a house, bought a car, fed his kids, stayed
out of jail. The right payback or compensation for a man's life,
however you pictured it, went missing, would never arrive. Might
this understanding—this slow-baked awareness of the lack of

an aging human's acknowledgment in the world, *by* the world—might this actually be the big punchline, the great magician's joke of American lives? Making the gold coin of meaning permanently disappear? It felt, even to a clueless kid, as if types like Clive had indeed somehow been cheated.

Maybe a simple nod was the hoped-for reward. Yet even that seemed missing.

And it appeared the same formula applied to women, only worse. Women hardly counted.

It seemed the world, hastening on, was bound by natural law to quickly forget its own.

Reason and Order

In my family's Juniper Street house, by contrast, we did not demonstrate rage.

We did not have arguments or protests or unpleasant words, not visibly.

Instead we held monthly sessions called Family Councils, when all of us convened in the living room and my sister and I and our father listened silently to our stepmother announce various household decisions. These included the posting of a daily chore list, handwritten on lined yellow legal paper, magneted to the refrigerator. The list's purpose was to eliminate any need for nagging. We girls were expected to complete several chores each day, so that the rooms of our modern house would remain severely clean.

The Hamlin house of course made no such demands, and its rooms offered a cheerful, consistent bomb-blast of chaos. Mismatched shoes and socks, toys, maps, dented canteens, corkboards, cups and tumblers, plates and bowls and vases, buttons, piles of clothes, board game tokens, pencils and crayons, crocheted blankets, popped caps for cap pistols, lengths of twine, plastic jewelry, books and newspapers, kerchiefs, coupons, skeins of yarn, pieces of unidentifiable plastic—scattered and piled everywhere. I'm guessing no one had cleaned the place since before the kids were born. They ate when they wanted, let Faith handle the aftermath, and were casual about the atmosphere being crazy—I mean, truly crazy. This was romantic to a fourteen-year-old. I liked running away to Mary's, slipping into a world without rules or expectations, escaping my own hyper-rational, hyper-ascetic home. It's easy to re-see that dreaded list—I knew its length by heart and could tell, even glancing from across the room, when new items had been added—those numbered tasks pressed hard onto yellow paper in ballpoint ink—vacuuming, dusting, scrubbing the shower glass with white vinegar, something I specially hated. (The acrid smell of vinegar still quick in memory's nostrils.) For me the two domiciles were two nations with antithetical laws, currencies, and even languages: the country of Hamlin a pleasant dump where there was always exciting stuff to eat and drink, odd and amusing distractions, and a kind of drifty laziness as its ambient ethos, an unspoken air of permissibility. You did what you liked, or not much: it was all the same. Ignored, unkempt, free. No tribunals, no summonses, no prosecutions, no interest except a genial, generic nod. Noise and motion issued at random, and at whim.

The worst punishment was Clive's rare, bitter, shuffling tours. If you were lucky you could dash off in time to avoid them, and return after they'd finished.

Cozy hiding-place, zero-gravity nest fallen outside time: the Hamlins'!

I would often wait for the moment when everyone else in our cool, quiet, orderly house seemed preoccupied—my father brooding over books and typewriter in his studio (the converted garage), preparing his classes; my stepmother primping with a frown at the big lit mirror of the vanity table in her bedroom; my sister on the phone, watching television, or eating cereal.

I'd call out to no one that I was going over to Mary's house, and not wait for an answer.

3

She's Not There

Mary appeared a moving-parts composite, a cubist painting—pieces fallen together—of so many things I wanted to be. How did we meet? Surely at the bus stop to high school, both of us just starting. She was impossible to miss. Tall and supermodel thin, the kind so prized at the time young girls everywhere were starving themselves to attain it. It was true that such a frame did not allow much in the way of breasts. But it was the era of Twiggy and Lauren Hutton and Jean Shrimpton, of Marianne Faithful and the young Vanessa Redgrave in the film "Blow Up." You didn't need breasts, at least not the kind that had been championed before. Even Diana Rigg as Emma Peel was a lithe, catlike thing. Gone into cold storage were Monroe, Ekberg, Mansfield. Mary was a dirty blonde, with wonderful straight, glossy hair that swung like heavy silk—another thing I envied almost as much as her lean body. I had thick fine brown hair, given to frizzing in the Sacramento winter fog. Many mornings I lay my head on the ironing board and pressed my long hair flat with a warm iron before school. The smell of burning hair wafted through the house, a gross wake of ill-gained illusion. And my poor hair would frizz right up again as I waited for the bus in the cold damp.

I might have met Mary walking home. The Hamlin Brigadoon was just a block from me.

Mary was an artist.

She made up designs for her own clothes, cut them out of cheap fabric, sewed them together: the bold cuts fell slinky and smooth on her lank body, straight and true. She painted and sketched and made cunning toys and dolls and sculptures of junk. She once sewed together a little stuffed rag-doll for me, from different patches of old-print material and red-yarn hair. (I can see its face and Raggedy Ann hair, its triangular, tiny-flower-print dress, this moment.) There seemed no object or surface, no shell or spangle or shard she could not make witty or useful. And Mary drew, and painted portraits: beautiful oval-faced young women, head-on, eye to eye, in the manner of Klimt or Modigliani (I now realize) and also of Picasso—I'm thinking of the Dora Maar portrait. But Mary often used Van Gogh's technique of many tiny strokes, communicating both energy and a certain anxiety: the images seemed to vibrate—also, to beseech. Her colors were rich and saturated, and often she made the *maquillage* of her faces denser and more theatrical by applying glitter, sequins, bits of sticks and leaves or fabric and string. I kept two of her paintings in my bedroom. Easily, invitingly, they promised something: a parallel life, some ideal bohemian universe we might successfully enter if we could just gather the right props. We shared, in fact, that vision—that dreamworld. We haunted the imports stores, coveting small, musty-smelling votive candles and incense; crudely carved wooden boxes with hinged lids, styled after medieval strongboxes and jewel caches. We favored black clothing. I dyed my hair black, played guitar, sang folk music. And the soundtracks of those years: Dylan, Baez, Gregorian chants, the Modern Jazz Quartet with Laurindo Almeida, Julian Bream, the Zombies, Left Bank, Django, Grappelli. If I could have afforded it, I'd have bought a harpsichord (advertised in high-end magazines) and learned to play "Lady Jane."

Mary blew in and out of classes, and teachers immediately disliked and distrusted her. She was sexual by apparent design and yet not, from any visible measure, by intent: she was that dreamy, that un-present. She made teachers nervous: everything about her seemed not so much to mock them as simply to have no use for them, or for the whole, prim, cement-block hothouse of high school. She slouched along the hallways, a tawny animal smiling with otherworldly serenity (yes, like lunatics on the street), as if carrying secret knowledge.

Oddly, this would never change.

Only one teacher saw into her without fear and liked her fine: an art teacher who later became famous for his hyper-intense photorealism—paintings of diner-booth condiments and aging, female nudes. He would lean against the doorjamb of his classroom, in the years we knew him, like a wry gunslinger, amused to watch students rush around.

Frankness, you could say, was his calling-card.

This teacher—dead now—much later moved East, to a converted carriage house. He had the wits and prescience to recognize and value Mary's art. The other teachers shook their heads ominously, because Mary ignored both her studies and their authority, blithely floating between classes (if she showed up at all) in a guileless trance, oblivious to the tittering, craven social cruelties of school, the gaggles of anxious girls—heedless of grades and similar measures of meaning or achievement. For the teachers she was the embodiment of the Wrong Road, and I couldn't help feel uneasy about this. I knew, in some chamber of myself, that things couldn't be that simple. It wasn't fair, I sensed even then, to divide future validity into neat camps of bad kids and good kids, the latter being chiefly defined by obedience. I could not then defend how Mary's sensual manner flustered men and women alike. I could only think of the song "Pretty Ballerina," by the band Left Bank, when I thought about Mary.

I fell in love with a pretty ballerina
Her hair so brilliant that it hurt my eyes
I asked her for this dance and then she obliged me
Was I surprised, yeah; Was I surprised, no not at all . . .

Long and pliant, straight hair swinging with her stride, half-smiling in that private thrall as if listening to invisible radio music—I could already see how men would soon be losing their minds for Mary, for the way her joints fit, the long ease of her hips and thighs. They would be reaching for her only to miss her somehow. She would slip their nets, elude them. We sang our favorite Zombies songs together.

Well let me tell you 'bout the way she looked, the way she acted,

the color of her hair. Her eyes were soft and cool, her gaze was clear and bright—

But she's not there!

With silent, sad resignation, I also understood in those fog-bound years that I served as a funky consort to Mary: clumsy second to her shining first. Mutt to her Jeff, Panza to her Quixote. I was shorter, fleshier: the brunette. I had language. I made words (often purple). I could sing and play guitar; spoke some French. But Mary made ravishing images. One lived with these understandings as an adolescent girl. The way the young discern such facts, the way they move mournfully ahead with that knowledge, giving no outward sign—like a farm animal in harness—strikes me now as a kind of through-line of ancient sorrow. But it also sobers me to recall that Mary never used her goddessness against me, never played mind- or ego-games, never lorded herself over me in any way. If I felt sad because I lost in the comparison of our appearances, she seemed cheerfully oblivious of such concerns. I don't remember a speck of opposition from her, no act or word that made me feel wrong. Perhaps we were both too intoxicated, soaked in half-formed dreams, too drifty in ourselves and the world—by default accepting the funny visual imprint we struck—to go against each other.

We would sit up in her little alcove bedroom, and hatch plans.

Let's go around the world together, I remember saying to her one day.

The notion sounded ripe and timely: round, bold.

We were sitting in Mary's loft—one of those mornings gearing up for hot but still carrying the leafy scent of coolness—facing each other, cross-legged, on the bed. Mary's bed was like one of Goldilocks' discoveries in a woods-deep cottage: gently rounded headboard and footboard painted with unfurling vines; bedding plump with piled quilts, all of it faded and softened by time. Clive had probably built those beds when Reeve was born, twenty-some years earlier. The room's loft ceiling sloped sharply on both sides. A woven-rag rug and small bureau; atop this a glittertrail of treasures: costume jewelry, eucalyptus acorns, several marbles (two pale blue clearies which I secretly prized), bottlecaps, a broken music box, tiny glass figurines. The window's wooden shutter flung wide to the sweet air, the massive oak's trunk touchable outside like a guarding nanny, sunlight and leaf-light dappling the walls.

Mary had been showing me her paintings, one by one. A little demonstration. Sitting up on her bed facing me, her long back to the headboard, she held each painting toward me in her lap, her face open and expectant, shy but pleased, giving me time to absorb and comment, lifting each piece away after my remarks to reveal the next, like giant flash cards. Outside the day would be brilliant, the big draping oak easily reached through the open window, our own beanstalk to scuttle down anytime we wished. The tree's dark leaves bounced patches of green light every which way; the air filled with bird-ruckus—squawking jays, crows, a mockingbird. All these small, sweet trappings must have framed, even urged, our clear belief. Both of us chafed, inchoately but powerfully, against a sense of invisible yet maddening confinement, of living in some equivalent of a crawl space, and each knew the other felt it though we had no language for it then; in our minds the door to the world, during those hours together, began to open. Mary's paintings and drawings groped for something neither of us could yet name.

Light and air, sweet and unfiltered floated from the window.

Okay, Mary was nodding. Let's agree to meet in a special place in a certain number of years.

No matter where we are then, or what we are doing, I said, leaning forward as I warmed to the idea, propped on clasped hands. We'll memorize the year and when it comes, we'll just stop everything. We'll remember. And we'll do whatever it takes to get to that place on that day.

Who else should we ask to meet us there? she asked.

We stared at each other. Neither of us knew many people then, or at least not well enough to extend such a freighted invitation.

I can't think of anyone, I said at last.

Other people probably wouldn't be serious and really do it, I said. They'd probably forget. Or get distracted.

Not us, though, said Mary. We'll remember.

Absolutely, I said, seeing all of it that instant, through gauze. We'll remember.

Where should it be? she wondered, stacking her paintings. The special place.

We went silent, thinking.

What about Paris? I said. It was the most famous place I could think of. I already loved (wept even to think about) the Victor Hugo novel.

What about Notre Dame Cathedral, I said. Anybody can tell us how to find it once we get there. We can just agree to meet inside the cathedral on a certain day of a certain year. And then never forget. And then on that day, whoever gets to the cathedral first can just take a seat in the back row and keep an eye on the main door, waiting for the other one to show up.

(I had not yet traveled to France. A big church was a big church.)

I thought some more.

Whoever gets there first, I repeated, keeps her eyes peeled for whoever is coming in.

And then she jumps up, and flags the other one down when the other one shows up.

Probably a bad idea to yell in church, I said.

Right, Mary said. Placing the tidied stack against the wall, she turned again toward me, cross-legged on the bed, with a little bounce. That's good. Yeah.

We were looking at each other, eyes ablaze with the brilliance of the vision. I'd slid off my end of the bed and begun stalking around. Crows and jays called through the window.

It'll be terrific, I said, thinking in all directions. We can wander around Paris together, after we meet up. You can paint. Maybe you can sell a few of them. That will help us buy food. I can write. Maybe I can be one of those guys on a street-corner who writes a letter or a poem for other people, for money. We'll meet people who'll let us crash on their floor. We can practice our French and—live there, maybe. We can live on bread and cheese. And wear . . . striped shirts.

Berets! Mary shouted, clapping her hands.

We'll go to the top of the Eiffel Tower, I said. People will love us. You can meet painters and I can meet writers. I'll bring my guitar. We can sing on streetcorners for extra money. Maybe we'll meet wonderful men. Maybe we'll never leave. We could become *citizens*.

It'll be perfect, Mary said. She smiled calmly. *Perfect* was the cherished word in those years, like cool and tough and bitchin', all of which meant *beyond wonderful*. I smiled back at my tall friend, fired with the symmetry of it; her lean torso and straight hair, her air of knowingness—exclusive possession. *Savoir faire*. She already looked the part completely. And somebody out there would recognize me for the female Kerouac I hoped to become, if I hadn't quite got there yet. They would think me perfect.

I peered out the window into the striated branches of the oak and listened to the songbirds, trying to see the future through the leaves and light. For the moment, I didn't mind being our zaftig, dark-haired scribe.

People would love us.

Hostile Season

In Sacramento, the heat took no pity.

As if a cruel giant held a magnifying glass between earth and sun. Slowly at first in May; by July it turned killer.

The Central Valley became a bowl of brown air; the hills, straw. A single match touched to those foothills would have sent curtains of flame sheeting up into the brittle old oaks and finally the lower pines leading to the mountains. Sometimes this did happen: it still happens. People living in the danger zones, then as now, watched the news nervously; emergency bags packed, hosing their roofs nightly, waiting for evacuation bulletins. The suburbs watched the news too, tensed, walking in and out of rooms eyeballing possessions, silently prioritizing them.

We sliced melon, drank can after can of discount diet cola. (It left the faint aftertaste of soap.)

Everybody napped a lot, or tried to.

It all felt science-fictiony: hostile season, alien planet. One obeyed the rhythms with an eye on escape.

Only early mornings held a breath of sweetness. Jays screamed at each other in the Japanese maple, birch, pyracantha; the sky, white-blue, turned pewter. Cut-grass, jasmine, and honeysuckle still sent sweet waves of fragrance. But you felt as much as knew, going out to pick up the newspaper from the already-warm pavement under your bare feet—the promise of murderous heat hung in the air, heavy and still. Trees drooped in the glare; leaves went wan and dusty. Birds cached themselves, invisible by late morning. Other animals found shade and lay down to pant in it.

Soon the air itself would seem to stop: so hot and dense and brown that if stranded in it, even briefly, you would begin to believe you were falling ill—heart pounded; sweat oozed; stomach fluttered. Familiar objects felt wrong: a cup, a hairbrush, the fabric of clothing. None delivered the heft, nor the temperature, the skin had come to expect.

Even the soles of the feet felt wrong—rubbery; numb.

It was weather to dull reasoning.

But Mary and I were young. So we dashed through it, shouting—across baking black tar and acrid concrete, hopping from one foot to the other in line at the Frostee Freeze, to the tennis-shoe-smelling locker room of the municipal pool, to the drugstore soda-counter for candy bars and colas under its sleepy ceiling fans—dashed unthinking; jubilant, as if answering a dare: coal-walkers.

Days Between

It couldn't have taken more than a week, immediately following my mother's death, for us to somehow get packed to move to California.

It was very hot then, too: September, Phoenix. The evaporative cooler whirred all day and night—a soft, steady, air-and-water threshing noise that gave me both a hollow feeling and a strange comfort—as if it were singing to me in one sustained breath, the only sound it owned, of how sorry but helpless it felt. And the living room became a receiving area where my father, akimbo in his nubbled easy chair as if shoved backward into it, absorbed the respects and sympathies of visitors, talking on and on.

The kitchen, a small, pink-tiled rectangle, filled soon with half-melted ice cube trays and foreign dishes that mystified us. Jellos with canned fruit and cottage cheese suspended inside. Gooey potato salads, casseroles—food we girls could not understand.

We wandered repeatedly from our bedroom to the living room where my father held court. My little sister and I were supposed to be trying to gather our clothing. We stared into our closet and bureau drawers—both closet and bureau now seeming, in my memory, so achingly small. Like sleepwalkers we began to lift items out, trying to assemble little piles on our beds. But we kept pausing to venture back into the living room, to make sure our father was still there.

Friends swooped in, I am fairly sure, to do most of the real work: to help us all pack, and to put the house up for sale. I have lost any visual memory of the steps of achieving that. I only remember my father, during those days, sitting stupefied in his throne talking to whomever was there, a drink always in his hand.

He drank whiskey and cola, or bourbon and cola, wine, beer,

whatever anyone brought.

In those days, liquor was the only solution.

Early September: hot, and very still. Air smelled of oleander flowers and hosewater.

I remember one of my father's friends during that time, an older woman, kneeling down before me at eye-level, in our living room. Fixing me with a clenched gaze, she intoned in a voice shaky and low:

You'll have to be very strong now.

These words frightened and sickened me. Though some part of me knew the woman meant to help, I could not imagine how I could not fail to be whatever it was she commanded. It felt like being pushed off the edge of any firm ground still beneath me, falling and falling. This, too, was surely some lack of mine. Ashamed, scared, nauseated, I could hardly meet her eyes.

Our pet dachshund was called Ruthie, and we girls loved her with all our hearts: chestnut-colored, softest fur, loving dark eyes, and my father determined she would come with us to our new life. A cage for the plane flight was sought.

One of his friends questioned the practicality of this, to which my father responded, "They've lost their mother. They'll have their dog."

4

Pilgrimage

One sweltering summer day, for no reason I can now recall except that it sounded round and big and significant, Mary and I decided we should walk to the Roseville Auction.

A superb thing. How good the words sounded. *We'll walk to the Roseville Auction.*

And after one of Faith's mammoth breakfasts—scrambled eggs, ham slices, toast from homemade loaves and muffins with red currant jam, hash browns, cups and cups of thickly-creamed-and-sugared coffee—Mary so lanky, me *zaftig,* straining my jeans—Faith mumbling and mewling as she wandered between stove and sink and stacked-up greasy platters—we staggered out the back door.

Saturday, sparkling-hot: we hoped to arrive in time for the livestock part that afternoon—the part, we figured, where the caller sings out in that strange nonstop yodel and the farmers somehow understand him, and make their bids for the animals with little casual nods and quiet hand-signals.

Auctioneering seemed exotic. Also, we thought, authentic—real, unaffected; a kind of life-marrow we were always seeking, nervously alert for, yet which in some ways we still could not quite fathom.

We'd never done anything like this before. We'd never spoken to anyone about it, or researched it. We just set out.

Mary found a path that paralleled the highway and we kept a good pace, talking about all we wanted someday to do; music, art, books; places we hoped to see. It was early enough that the heat had not yet tightened into a stranglehold, and our resolve felt sturdy and calm. Sometimes we found ourselves walking along behind housing tracts: you could see into each backyard, all the scattered props at the rears of people's homes, gardens, kiddie swings, barbecues, doghouses, baby pool, rabbit pens, washing pinned to lines, strewn toys. Sometimes hysterical dogs flung themselves at chain link fences, yawping and howling as we passed. The bordering trees bent over us, eucalyptus, oak, birch. Summer wildflowers spread around the dry scrub like confetti, tiny purple-whites, pinks and blues like miniature orchids—generous stands of brilliant orange California poppies, whose velvet petals reminded you of butterfly wings. In the undeveloped stretches, acacia trees, mesquite, creosote. I specially loved the big dusty manzanita bushes—unremarkable at first glance, their leaves little furls of crust—because (on second glance) their trunks and bark sworled deep umber-red, as uncannily smooth to the touch as my father's cherrywood pipe.

The morning sun climbed and surged. Stillness seemed our only witness. We pushed north following the railroad tracks, and after a time found ourselves crossing through an old switching yard. Impossible to resist pausing to wander among the giant, dead carriages, trying to guess their histories while staring at their dusty sides, unable to decipher the welter of graffiti and markings. The cars stood petrified, huge, rusting, a graveyard of stiff dinosaurs. Train workers had scrawled numbers and codes on them in chalk or spray paint—alas, no poetry, no mystical instructions—and the dried-up grass and corroded tracks beneath them released no secrets. No doors slid open the way they did in movies—so that we might slip inside and be carried away, with other runaways, to the hobo camps where rakes and rogues sang and told stories around the fire. As we stepped between the cars, squinting at their scratched paint and forgotten symbols, at the scars and bruises the elements had left upon them, we listened, too: the silence was overpowering; only the barest stir of air under the unblinking sun, punctured by an occasional fly's buzz, and our own murmurs of longing.

For this wandering life, we told each other, was the source. This was the way to find one's way, find things out: everything waited to be found out. O to be a train-car bum, the ultimate artist-rover, to see life and country—the real country, not just the touristy hotels and plastic facades. I would be on the lookout for the likes of Pete Seeger and Arlo Guthrie, for the wily Dylan and his goddess-consort Baez—for all those Robin Hoods doing the right work; bearing messages of what was real and true. Wherever we went (reprising my projections for our guaranteed success in Paris) Mary could paint portraits for pocket money; I could write letters or poems on the spot, for people's occasions. I'd carry my dad's Royal portable typewriter, his gift to me, in its handsome tweedy case (never mind how awkward that might prove). We burned to do all of it—but with no immediate prospects for hitching a ride on any train in that warm, abandoned yard, we strode on.

It grew hotter still, and we were sweating but unfazed; we must have walked twenty miles that day. Mary led us through vacant lots, alleyways, pastures, fields, pebbly backroads. At last, around noon, we crested a hill and beheld, in the hazy distance, what looked like a biblical encampment: the quilt-like spread of many sizes of tents and lopsided temporary storefront-shacks and shelters, amid moving crowds and kicked-up dust and acres of glinting parked cars.

We had arrived.

Marketplace

The auction's smells were State Fair smells, arousing, gritty: frying burgers, potatoes, onions, corndogs, dust and leather and hay, sawdust and manure, burnt-sugar smells of cotton candy and cola, root beer and kettlecorn, glistening-fat smells of sausages and chili-dogs, salt-steam of roasted nuts, banks of barbecued chickens turning and dripping on rotisserie spits, yeasty pong of fry-bread and beer and soft pretzels, boiled-bitter-grounds smell of coffee, rind-and-crushed-leaf smells of fresh melons, oranges, strawberries, tomatoes. Sounds, too, were carnival sounds: midway barkers, fruit and vegetable sellers calling out, wailing babies and whining kids, scolding parents, flirting and arguing lovers, complaining cattle (the livestock section took up the western side of the gathered tents), mooing and lowing that rose now and then into an indignant shriek, annoyed or frantic pigs, irritated sheep and goats, panicked hens and throttled screeching roosters (baby chicks under heat lamps in boxes, their peeps like tiny muffled bells), radios blaring country music, early Beatles, Elvis, Chuck Berry, Patsy Cline. Canvas booths set up in long rows created little neighborhoods, dirt-and-sawdust streets: along these in two directions roamed noisy packs of humans, brows sweating and cheeks mottled, bellies swelling over waistbands, kerchiefs knotted across foreheads, sleeves cutting into armflesh.

Mary and I stepped straight into it, pleased to be swept along, looking and looking. The auction was no mirage; it felt alive, and the two of us with it.

What goods the farm families sold—we never asked ourselves where or how they acquired any of it—fell toward us, a feast of tawdriness and mystery. Levis jeans in every size (including double-large), board-flat, so starched from the factory they stacked like tiles. Heavy sweatshirts with hoods and front pockets bearing phony college names and letters. T-shirts stenciled with patriotic slogans or lewd jokes or dope-dealer cartoons. Heaps of worthless gimcracks, the sort you found on drugstore turnstiles or in dig-through-it-yourself pyramids or pinned to makeshift front counters in their crackly clear plastic—kid handcuffs, squirt guns, yo-yo's, sets of jacks, erasers, candy cigarettes, pop beads in multiple pastels, fake fangs, Groucho-nose-and-eyebrow-glasses, sparkle-paints, paddle-balls, harmonicas, colored pencils, little-girl jewelry sets and nail polish, glow-in-the-dark rubber balls, invisible ink pens, fake turds, fake vomit, squeaky bathtub animals, fart cushions, rabbit's foot keychains, miniature Slinkies, boxes of gum, plastic jars of bubble-blowing liquid (wands inside), neon-frame sunglasses, wax lips, and a gorgeous slew of wind-up toys—chattering teeth, waddling penguins, seals spinning tiny balls on their noses. And grownup toys interleaved with them: Christmas ornaments, ceramic figurines and ashtrays, lava lamps, wind chimes, plastic dinner sets, potholders, teapot covers (in that heat!), hemp doormats, macramé hangings and planters. Matchbox-sized music-box mechanisms that played the first few bars of a song when you turned its tiny crank: Claire de Lune, You Are My Sunshine, Over the Rainbow. One booth was piled with old 45 rpm records and albums. Mary and I drifted to the secondhand and antiques tents, where a few shrewd scavengers hoped to offload what they'd gathered from garage and estate sales.

Detritus of human lives.

When you are young—maybe all your life—you are both repelled by and attracted to this morbid tableau: drawn by curiosity, leary lest its unanswerable sadness stall or waylay or somehow infect you.

Here (these objects insist) *is what we do.*

Here is what we prize, what we wish for, fish for.

Quickly, though—so it seems—passersby lose interest, and cast the stuff aside.

I remember coming upon a small wind-up clock of tarnished brass (I pretended it was dulled gold) sitting pertly inside its own little form-fitted, fake-leather case that snapped shut with a delectable click. I can see it still, attached to its fittings like a clam to its shell, the closed case nesting snugly in my fist. A cheap travel clock, Arabic numbers painted on in plain typeface, phosphorescent chartreuse implying it would glow in the dark. (It didn't.) In my fantasies the clock was a magic heirloom: a turn-of-the-century pocket-watch with possible time-travel powers. (Where do these dreams come from? Movies?) At some level I *wanted* that clock to whisk me backward—to a striped-wallpapered parlor where men's bowlers hung on polished hooks during elaborate teas, where tepid beer was snuck into cached tumblers while no one looked. I bought the little clock for seventy-five cents and kept it many years, though it stopped working almost immediately.

That day, too, I was drawn as if by magnetic force to a bin packed with box after box of unframed photo portraits from early in the century: many sepia, some black and white. (Who made it their business to raid the homes of the dead for this stuff? I did not think about it then. I did not think this way at all then. Matter just *manifested* before you for your amusement when you were young, like scenery outside a moving car or train—then disappeared from existence when it left your sight.) I leafed through the photos, growing dizzy, unable to stop. Most of them bore no caption. Some were thin and cracked. Many smelled of mildew. No handwriting named these posed individuals or their ages, or the year the pictures had been taken. Subjects looked into the recording camera's eye with an expression I have all my life found difficult to describe, and which all my life has distressed and mesmerized me.

Couples posed in rigid formality: him seated, hat balanced on a knee, hair carefully parted and combed; her just behind his shoulder—her hand sometimes resting lightly on that shoulder. They wore what would have been their best clothes—looking starched and uncomfortable—corset-tight dresses, high-necked collars and scratchy wool suits; self-conscious loop of a watch-chain. They sat or stood beside a lamp or table, or plain curtains or a sheet. Eyes gazed evenly into mine: what speared me was a setness about the mouths, a numbness in the eyes. Their faces bore a terrible resignation. Sometimes their eyes seemed to dare mine to dispute what I was seeing: Their suffering.

I'm trapped here, their eyes said.

There's no recourse. I'm making this record of it.

Looking at them, I would feel choked with a kind of aroused panic, a voyeur's guilt. But I could not take my eyes from their faces. They felt so close to me in time, age, temperament. Surely their thoughts had been like mine. I could have known any of them, could have *been* them. It seemed sheerest accident that I was not. Why had they arrived on earth that arbitrary number of years before me, when on the earth's surface we seemed so alike? What was it they seemed to be telling me? Pair after pair of dazed eyes. Did they warn, silently and posthumously, of something I faintly suspected but could never clarify? What could I do about it? What could I do for them? Motion and noise and dirt of the carnival around me receded. On I pored through the packs of dulled film veined with cracks, the square- and oval-framed faces, the glassy, stoic eyes: surely once the denizens of those old Victorian homes I'd so often passed, of who-knew-what migrations. My prickling skin—waves of bumps even in that heat—told me their lives had not been long, nor easy. Witnesses and prisoners, even those who, on the surface of that world, had prospered, now lost, utterly forgotten. Layer after internal layer peeled away rapidfire. I understood that the people I walked and lived among now, the dusty sweaty greasy roar of families, farmers and grifters and barkers—even my ascetic home's secret rages and griefs, its off-limits food drawer and yellow-pad chore list—all that, too, would soon, somewhere, be gazing out at a disinterested stranger as part of a pile of inscrutable images.

One day, so would I.

The Long Day Closes

Then Mary was suddenly beside me, amid the heat, the voices, the clucking and clanging and lowing, which all then came vrooming back; a rush.

Look! Do you like it?

She twirled around: she had found an old black velvet cape, with a loose hood that hung from the back of the neck: the sort you tied at the front, the comely-female-client-of-Sherlock-Holmes sort. And though the stifling air under those dust-coated tents and crowds of sweating people made it incongruous as an Inuit parka, Mary swirled with it pulled about her shoulders so it flared out and I could admire it. It was wonderfully right for her, and I—giddy with relief at being yanked from the death-stares of the photographs—told her so. She could wear it in Paris! This pleased her deeply; her smile was triumphal. We carried our treasures in cheap plastic sacks through the fair, staying the whole day, watching the auctioneer gabble his singsong over cows and sheep, under a big open shelter with a canvas roof, big as a warehouse, smelling of hay and sawdust, mud and dung; the creatures bleating their displeasure, tails switching flies; farmers squinting, smoking, impassive as poker players in faded denim jackets and caps with *John Deere* embroidered on the front.

We lingered at the record booths, their raucous competing soundtracks and posters of rock musicians; lingered at every façade til we'd seen our fill, strolling and drinking root beer and pink lemonade, eating peanut brittle and squaw bread.

It baffles me now that, intensely as I concentrate on that day, and by inference those years, intensely as we both felt things, I am not able to remember a single cross word between us, Mary and me.

I honestly believe there was none.

I recall only her attentive, clear, wickedly-lit eyes and that manic, knowing smile in her strange, old-lady face—an element of Mary's appearance I've not yet thoroughly described here, or ever quite understood. Perhaps because her skin was pocked, Mary's face always looked aged, even back then. Her long body was one thing, tilting back as we walked—a swimsuit model's, the Ipanema Girl's—and it automatically drew everyone's gazes.

Her face was something else. This didn't register in me, then, as a thing to dwell on.

We were too caught up in the swirling world at hand. We laughed and marveled, told each other stories, sang, refined our plans.

I remember walking home together as if in the closing scenes of a movie: single file we tramped along the dirt-path rim of a canal as evening fell, the dark water striped with brass light, tired and dreamy under a sky sashed with grey, blue and scarlet, while the at-last-exhausted sun dropped behind the land's edge. A pinpoint first star appeared, like a touched chime. I remember feeling the sweet, tired, swept-empty peace that fills the chest and belly after you have laughed a long time. And then I remember, on arrival to my own house, how the dream curdled: my father scolded me severely because I had forgotten an appointment to babysit, for a local family, that very night. I felt miserable, wretched for my carelessness, but I felt worst for my hapless father, who'd had to endure the anger of the young parents in search of me, which of course he'd never deserved. Like many a young person before and after me, I could not explain nor understand my own stupidity, as frankly baffled by it as I was ashamed of it. I took without protest my punishment of being sent to bed without supper. Probably, I told myself, I was an evil person. And yet, thoughtless and foolish and utterly selfish as I knew my forgetting to have been—I couldn't feel evil.

I couldn't indict myself, except for having inadvertently hurt my bewildered father.

No clear sense of monstrousness flowed through me. I hadn't meant to act in an evil way. But my lack of consciousness, itself, suggested otherwise.

Saddened, I could only dwell with this.

I had no excuse. I'd been swept away with Mary.

5

North Beach

Because the Hamlins had no money, hitchhiking became the only way the children could travel.

Travel, in turn, was the only way we kids could enter the world, investigate the world, participate in the world. One midwinter day—damp, drizzly fog, dark gray—Mary and I conceived a splendid new project: we would hitchhike to North Beach in San Francisco. Where the Beats met! I hoped to smack headfirst into Kerouac (or his ilk). He—or his prototype or stand-in—would recognize me at once, sweep me up bridal style, run with me in his arms to Ocean Beach: straight into the icy water, where we would splash and scream and build a bonfire on the beach to dry off and drink cheap wine to get warm with people just like us, and shout and sing with joy.

And Mary? How can I speak for her here without reducing her? Surely her main thought, like mine, was for adventure: some blurry idea of it. At that time, I sensed that she could take or leave men—any man. It wasn't that she cared for women. Like me, she hadn't yet wakened to desire for men; mild curiosity was all we had. These were the sixties. Adult men—straight men—still regularly wore suits and hats, like Fred MacMurray and Herb Caen. Mary and I put on jeans and sweaters. I pressed my hair. We walked out onto the entrance to the interstate and bravely put out our thumbs. At once a woman stopped for us, a suburban housewife. Her face tense with worry, she questioned us anxiously, concerned that we could have been her own children. We bore her anxiety calmly, secure in our smug, untried, immortal, clueless certainty.

What had I told my father and stepmother? Some shameless camouflage. Had they known—had *he* known—his hair would have turned to pure snow. (It was salt and pepper then.) She'd have shrugged. I knew, even then, that everything I did enervated and vexed her.

Damp, cheerless cold, like Berlin in some dour art film. All color vanished; sky packed low, darkstreaked clouds pressing close, everything brown and charcoal—miles of the usual artless, dumb stretch of Soviet gloom. Yet to us in that time, such a bled, bleak setting only stoked the romance of our vision—kingdoms by the sea, candles, carved strongboxes, glittering beads, long gowns and long hair, Guinevere and Camelot (but somehow, magically, a Camelot where no one suffered), harps and harpsichords, hearths and flutes and shanties, the Kinks and Left Bank: Europe and fountains, secret gardens and staircases and attics, Impressionists, handsome rogue suitors, sing ho for the life of a sailor. My favorite painting was Renoir's lush, laughing *Luncheon of the Boating Party*; Mary's was Picasso's jangled *Les Desmoiselles D'Avignon*. All these years later, I see this crossroads of tastes and untried love standing for exactly what it had to. Why should I, or anyone, unwish that? The quest was everything. Barren winter framed it; gray skies cossetted its jewel heart like cotton batting—brought out the ruby's flame-lit center.

Past the flat rice fields we rode, past the naked orchards, black branches of pear and plum and peach trees in the Dixon farm belt, past the roadside stands for fresh-squeezed juice, for pistachios, olives, pickles, dried figs. Then Vacaville, a bland waspy suburb sprouting bleak hotels and coffeeshops along the freeway. Then Vallejo with its military-housing ambience and more faceless malls with jutting signs and military wives driving station wagons—but never mind all that because the ocean was near: you could already smell it through the windows, a thrilling rough algae-salt-stink that made inlanders giddy. Past the wet mudflats of Berkeley with their witty abstract stick-sculptures, over the grimy Bay Bridge—at the left the ugly shipyards of Oakland, where all the goods came that pumped an increasing prosperity into the westernmost edge of the continent, cars and machinery from the Far East, cane sugar and pineapple from Hawaii, plastic and soybeans and containers loaded with cheap junk. On the right, green-black freezing East Bay water, covered with tiny white chops like goosebumps; at a distance, the lonely eyeless fortress Alcatraz, surreal as if pasted on. Behind it, blood-dark spikes of Golden Gate Bridge poking up through fog. After lengths of passage in various cars driven by confused commuters, men who glanced at us with nervous curiosity, a sort of embarrassed tension—aware perhaps that we were being insanely naive in some time-honored way and who (blessedly, miraculously) resolved, against whatever inchoate impulses, not to intervene— we found ourselves walking Columbus Avenue along that Irish-turned-Italian patch called North Beach, smelling of garlic and coffee and wine, gasoline and exhaust fumes and rain-wet concrete, just a few blocks from the piers and ferry building and Fisherman's Wharf and the seagulls cawing over a briny bay.

All my life I have marveled at the life of Columbus, a wide, brazen, tawdry, teeming street that stood then (far less now if still, half-assedly, symbolically) as the artery of the bohemian sector. But as a young woman I found it monumental, looming, impossibly alive, glistening and textured, a writhing dragon. The series of windows along its filthy sidewalks gave over into musty, cavelike worlds holding ancient secrets: bric-a-brac shops, record album and thrift shops; postcard shops, ceiling-to-floor showcases of bizarre and vulgar art; black-light posters; coke-spoon collections; marijuana paraphernalia; antique velvet dresses and leather bondage costumes, magicians' stores stuffed with stale, brittle props, card decks, tricks and toys. Yeasty beeriness breathed from bars, old jukebox music filtering out, halfhearted barkers shifting from foot to foot, smoking, haggard, listless and bored in front of the topless bars. The wet-wood-and-wool smell of City Lights Bookstore, where we prowled creaky narrow aisles and zigzagging staircases. I looked up my favorites, Kerouac and Cassidy, Brautigan and Bukowski—though the latter wrote about women in ways that made me feel a little sick. Ferlinghetti himself was nowhere to be seen, but we tingled to think the poet might stroll through at any minute. Anyone might. In the watery light, in a narrow aisle of damp wood shelving, I opened *A Coney Island of the Mind* to "The

Dog Trots Freely in the Street," whose lines—even then I saw—
embodied exactly the sturdy cheer and brisk, democratic equability
of a city-scouting dog, a pervading anthem, and I felt something in
the center of my chest soften.

The dog trots freely in the street

and sees reality

and the things he sees

are bigger than himself

and the things he sees

are his reality

Drunks in doorways

Moons on trees

The dog trots freely thru the street

and the things he sees

are smaller than himself

Fish on newsprint

Ants in holes

Chickens in Chinatown windows

their heads a block away

The dog trots freely in the street

and the things he smells

smell something like himself

The dog trots freely in the street

past puddles and babies

cats and cigars

poolrooms and policemen

He doesn't hate cops

He merely has no use for them

and he goes past them

and past the dead cows hung up whole

in front of the San Francisco Meat Market

He would rather eat a tender cow

than a tough policeman

though either might do

And he goes past the Romeo Ravioli Factory

and past Coit's Tower

and past Congressman Doyle

He's afraid of Coit's Tower

but he's not afraid of Congressman Doyle

although what he hears is very discouraging

very depressing

very absurd

to a sad young dog like himself

to a serious dog like himself. . .

Frying onions and garlic everywhere, from the Bohemian Cigar Store that served sandwiches on focaccia bread, to the dozens of crowded little Asian and Italian diners giving cheap, delicious food all day without fanfare—spaghetti and a tumbler of wine for a handful of coins. People burst along the sidewalks, everyone (this, always, the mystery of cities) so urgent, purposive, so certain of their missions! (What would happen, I wonder a lifetime later, if anyone's mission were thwarted, halted in its tracks?) Gray and cold meant nothing here. The movement, the noise (car wheels shisssing on rain-wet streets, calls of barkers, streetcorner violinist with matted case open for change, gasping out one of the Vivaldi seasons). Steams and vapors—coffee-brandy-rum, mildewing books, cigars, diesel fumes—and lights: chromelight, window Christmas lights never taken down, oil rainbows on wet asphalt, blue neon, green, red, gold ricocheting—impatient horns of straining traffic—all of it a bloodstream, rushing.

We walked and looked, eyes gulping and misting.

And famous Vesuvio's, narrow as a train-car (everything in North Beach narrow, squeezed, chockablock, an elaborate ant-colony)—its glassed-in bar like a human aquarium where from the street you could watch people sitting quietly, legs crossed, talking over Irish coffees or staring (as if into a crystal ball) into cups of wine or shots of whiskey or clear martinis with single olives, gelid and austere. Then at Broadway the Carol Doda place, where a bigger-than-life neon woman with gigantic breasts, nipples big as your head flashing neon-fuschia, laughing eternally. (This sight gave me first inklings of how the sex game—I was only beginning to grasp its size and power—could be played: some women connived to harness the ubiquitous animal force and make it work, nominally, to give them money. I admired the angry ingenuity of this—but also felt, deep beneath it, something so desolately lonely I had no words for it.) All along Broadway, we passed pimps and hustlers for the nude shows; they kept up a halfhearted patter, the way baseball players harass whomever's up to bat. Mary and I had never seen a strip show; the very words still shocked us though we'd never admit that. We wandered dazed, breathless, heads swiveling: first-time rafters on a swift and swollen Amazon.

Come in. Come see the show, said a mild-faced young man, nodding and smiling at us.

He had a slight accent, Germanic sound to it. Viennese? Softer than German. German sounded, I'd always thought, like the speaker was hocking up something, and it made me a little afraid from all the war films I'd seen.

I'll give you half-price, he said. The young man's smile and manner were gentle, almost wan. He was nice to look at. Fair hair, neatly cut and combed; pleasant body not too large or small but with a manly shape, clean, quietly dressed. A jacket, pressed shirt, trousers. His face, I could see, was kind, and the clamoring swirl of Broadway and Columbus muted and faded back as I considered him, stopped by the gentleness in his eyes. Were they blue or gray?

He had a companion barker friend, taller and darker, and Mary was smiling at this companion.

But we're—I did not say the word *underage*. I saw that he knew, but he would, he said, make it possible. He had a soft urgency. Sadly, I understand now that he was likely paid (whatever pitiful wage) by the head-count. A dark curtain fell behind him, and he and his tall friend promised to escort us in and have a drink with us. We ducked with them behind the dusty curtain through a brief, dank concrete passage and into a makeshift *boîte*, a low-ceilinged, crudely-rigged basement. Before us, a scattering of tables and a stage, and the space smelled of what I now know to be the worldwide, sorrowful-old-basement-bar smell: stale liquor, halfhearted cleaning fluid, years of smoke and body odor and rancid perfumes; olfactory ghosts laid one on top of the next for eons, a burial ground. We sat at a table set far back from the stage in the darkest part of the cave—so as not to be noticed and caught out, I guessed, though it didn't seem anyone saw or cared. The table was a telephone-wire spool turned sideways, sticky with old beer. I didn't know what to order. I remembered that gin and tonic was something adults spoke of so I asked for that, and when it came in a skinny glass it looked pale blue and smelled and tasted like aftershave cologne with ice in it. The stage had dingy curtains behind and on either side of it; a few lights at its low forefront threw harsh yellow beams like headlights.

Suddenly, recorded music squawked on.

A woman wearing a spangly sort of ice-skating costume, pink and yellow, trimmed with what looked like strips of old fur, trailing dust-colored feather boas, sashayed out while a sinuous jazz saxophone's notes issued from a record player's cached speakers. The woman also wore a blonde wig and false eyelashes; she had orangey lips and cheeks. (I now can't help visualize the underlit, corpse-makeup faces of the onstage dancers in Toulouse-Lautrec.) To me the woman was old: perhaps 40. And this made me understand, in a wrenching stroke, too many anguishing things about the straits of women and men. The spotlights from below threw shadows above her heavily-rouged cheeks into the hollows of her eyes, so that her eyesockets looked empty. The club was quiet and nearly deserted. A few unfeatured beings sat at tables close to the stage; tendrils of cigarette smoke dissolved toward the ceiling from each ashtray like smoke from incense—but these human forms were indistinguishable in the bluish dark around the hard lights.

The woman, smiling her clown-painted smile, walked back and forth on the stage—haltingly, as if reminding herself she was supposed to do that—accompanied by the sax music which sounded like the room itself: smoky, louche, listless. Every so often she would unzip a glove, or a little piece of her pink and yellow skating costume and work these pieces off while walking unsteadily back and forth. (It only occurs to me now she might've been drunk or drugged.) She kept the feather boas on over the other pieces of clothing she was losing—they floated after her like lengths of decrepit Christmas tree garlands—never letting go of the smile, the kind of smile you muster when someone is taking much too long to snap your photo and your patience is used up and the sun is shrieking directly into your eyes. Except it was dank and chilly down there: wasn't the lady cold? We sat at our table, watching. No one made a gesture or sound in that near-empty basement, and I was conscious, sipping watery-cold aftershave, of my own confusion. Finally the lady had only a g-string on. The word *g-string* was a nasty word in the known world at that time, and now here it was, an actual g-string. I saw that it was in fact a kind of Kotex belt without the Kotex. I don't remember now whether her pubic hair was shaved off or just too minimal to notice. I only knew the lady's body seemed saggy and yellow in the stage-light, not the balloony pink kind I'd seen in the Playboy centerfolds my girlfriend's father pinned up in his den. The lady's breasts seemed smallish and tired. They looped down and slightly out, like little L's, nothing at all like the centerfold's breasts—surely, anyway, her breasts were cold in that frigid cellar.

At last her act was done. A few sets of hands slowly began

to clap. *Plack, plack, plack-plack*—our own escorts' hands dutifully placking as the lady walked off the stage, having abandoned all effort to sashay; she bent like a tired mother to scoop costume items from the stage floor, where they now looked like scrambled eggs with thousand island dressing. She had dropped the pinched smile; what remained on her face was a vacancy. Whatever filled a face with some fundamental human presence had left hers completely: you couldn't guess who may once have dwelt there.

Blinking, we crept back through the mildewed passage into the gray day and rain-reflected lights of the street, and my new friend suggested I visit his room with him. I agreed to this, cheerfully circling the prospect that I was probably going to kiss him. Mary, meantime, happily agreed to go visit her tall friend's room with him. We must have arranged to meet afterward, and to this moment I am filled with utter wonder by the memory, astonished by our innocence and luck. I remember lying down with the young man on his narrow single bed, in a tiny room like a jail cell with a high, barred, garret-style window. All of this episode is leached of color: dirt-gray, pigeon-gray light sifted through. The young man, whose name is forever lost from that long-ago day, lay on top of me briefly, fully clothed, and we kissed. We never removed our clothing—perhaps it was too cold; perhaps our bodies did not insist upon it. At some point both of us seemed to comprehend there was no reason to continue kissing, and it was time for me to leave. He was calm and sweet bidding me goodbye, this young man, and he was *still kind, the whole while*. Dear gods and stars—if that once-young-man is alive today (oh, he would be so old!) and somehow, somewhere reading and recognizing any part of this, I take both his aged hands in mine and kiss them to thank his younger self for sparing that ridiculously, dangerously reckless young girl.

On the street I found Mary, waiting, smiling, unfazed—and without needing or wishing to speak of whatever we had privately encountered we found the necessary streets, and sought and accepted the necessary series of rides home—again, wondrously, given all we now understand and have witnessed—without event.

Men who gave us rides looked at us, I recall, with a kind of pain. Something almost imperceptible in them seemed to hesitate—and check itself.

It is possible that those men had daughters, or nieces or other female relatives of an age to remind them. It is possible that we simply happened into a series of human beings who decided, against other urges, to take the high road.

None harmed or touched us. None spoke to us in an untoward way.

As simple, as improbable, as life- and soul-saving, as that.

In Your Place

Our father told us she'd had a heart attack in her sleep.

Twenty years later, I telephoned several close friends of my late parents—all very old by then.

One, a man who'd been close to my father, said in a catching, wavering voice: "In your place, I'd want to know."

Another, a woman who'd known them both well, spoke carefully into the phone from her remote seaside town:

"It is possible your mother just wanted some sleep."

6

Running Away

As is the way of things—especially in childhood alliances—Mary and I began to lose each other.

I loved my high school classes; found refuge there.

They were almost too easy for me, therefore easy to become a kind of egghead-star. It comforted me to float in the soft, silent ether of this envelope of specialness, though I also grew more lonely.

In the dailiness of these rounds, so mild on their surface, I could not yet imagine escaping—let alone oppose—what was expected of me.

So I performed: chores and homework, essays and tests, babysitting and housecleaning, applications to colleges. I was diligent. At the same time, a strange bifurcation overcame me: I could not feel that the *I* who was performing these dutiful functions so excellently had much to do with the *I* who perceived the ways she was expected to perform.

This splitting-down-the-middle, as if watching myself in a continuous film over which I had no control, going through expected motions and uttering expected sounds, suggested to me (at the time) that I was a fraud, or going mad, or both.

There was no one to whom I could confide this knotty, bereft sense of guilty meta-awareness, of alien-ness, of numbness: for all my deft powers of language I could scarcely articulate it to myself. I drifted into a self-generated mist of exile, out of which I stepped from time to time to try to date boys—to make some stab at the choreography of what I guessed to be the life of a normal teen-aged girl, hoping that function would follow form.

I dated athletic types who wore wool Pendleton shirts and doused themselves with Jade East and English Leather. How we even talked, I can't imagine. Probably we hardly talked.

I kissed them and pressed up against them—hoping to absorb their wholesomeness.

(How inexpressible all this felt.)

By contrast, Mary seldom bothered with classes. She drifted down the halls alone, dreaming. She dated older boys who had nothing to do with school, who were therefore never seen. I imagined them as Brandos or Belmondos wearing leather jackets, impenetrably sinister with a worldliness I could not pretend to understand. I presumed that Mary was having sex with them, which unnerved me. Was she safe? Was she knowing more than the rest of us? I had for some time stopped visiting the Hamlin house, confused and afraid. I assumed she'd mock me, all my apple-polishing and rule-abiding. And as high school came to an end I glimpsed less and less of Mary's languid, leaning-back form (like a Calder mobile with loose components in independent motion—or like one of *Les Desmoiselles* themselves). At some point she seemed to have altogether disappeared. A low surge of shame prickled me every time I drove past the Hamlin house—I had learned to drive, in a battered, split-pea-soup-colored Volkswagen bug handed down to me—each time I rounded the grassy rise at the corner off Juniper Street, cloaked by the draping oak. Sometimes I saw old cars parked on the Hamlins' steep drive. Sometimes I glimpsed Gus's portly white chest and suspicious side-eye, waddling and flapping on patrol. Once or twice I caught sight of Tommy, taller and now noticeably handsome in the way of Reeve, shuffling on or off the school bus. (Rumors had it that Tommy was drinking then, wandering through school flat drunk. Ah, but I was so self-immersed I could hardly pay attention, and told myself nothing could ever surprise me from those Hamlins.)

Kids have a way of suddenly deciding to shun each other. It's almost a pheromone–adults are baffled by the invisible signal of it like a soundless dog-whistle—a toggle of tacit will. No preamble;

no action or word; no aftermath.

Whatever it was that had once drawn me to the Hamlin house—I understood this in some unformed, unsaid way—I could no longer afford to indulge it. A dark, drowning sinkhole image had begun to define the place to me, in my chaotic thinking (blurts of half-reasoned instinct). I started to fear that if I got too close that sucking spout might pull me under irreversibly, and I'd be snuffed like a bug in syrup. On reflection, I believe I feared that the paper-thin scaffolding, supporting some feeble construct of a self, would be ripped down by the heavy hopelessness of the Hamlin air; any conceivable future for me thereby also lost. I'd lose power to think or act or leave, to push off, gain velocity (and nerve) to launch beyond Juniper Street. How this primal dread took hold and built on itself, I can't say. I remember a fear of being slowly consumed and nullified there, paralyzed by the inert bog of the Hamlin life—a place where you fell out of time into the soft sleepy sticky goo of their numberless days, yammerings, meals and spats and meaningless errands and never, ever any money—half-ignorant arguments nudged on by cheap wine and coffee and later weed; arguments about insoluble vagaries that fell away without result or resolve. Nullity, nullity, stasis. Once caught, instinct told me, I'd stay stuck.

Like trying to run in a dream.

I left home to go to college, cheaply, down the road. After a couple of years, still in the grip of a self-convicted fraud's horrified guilt, I left college to join the Peace Corps in West Africa.

Still later, giving up on performance, I settled in Hawaii. Somehow, I managed during those years to briefly visit Europe; even Tahiti.

My father died suddenly, at fifty-four.

I worked many jobs, fell in love. I lost those loves. These are long chapters for elsewhere.

I began, haltingly, to write.

By the time I was thirty I was rooming with two divorced women in a wealthy suburb on an Oahu hilltop, overlooking the zillionaire beachfront real estate called Kahala and beyond it, the gray-green sea. I worked, by then, at a friend's downtown Honolulu office. At some level not quite yet conscious I was preparing to return, after a dozen years away, to the American mainland. There were two children where I lived, in that Maunalani Heights house, a dog, ex-husbands and boyfriends cycling through, the atmosphere that of a hastily-rigged campsite. I was living out of a suitcase and sleeping on the couch.

Change was bearing down.

A Phone Call

One teal-blue evening one of my Maunalani housemates drifted into the kitchen—where I often stood staring out the window, drinking instant coffee, feeling frightened and sick about my life and prospects, as usual—to call me to the phone.

It's someone named Mary Hamlin, my housemate said. Long distance.

These recollections—please know—are drawn from memory's half-light. The scenes dissolve at their edges faster and faster with accelerating years, like disintegrating film. And the dissolution process also works inward; time and fatigue start to blot out associated feelings like cataracts, fading color and detail: what's left becomes bland generality. I hasten to sketch what identifiable fragments remain, as they, too, go translucent.

The first image to come rushing forward in mind, at the announcement of that waiting phone call, was Mary's face.

There is no polite way to convey this fairly. I've hinted at it earlier but the effect in real time is as tricky to understand as it may have been in hindsight. Mary's was the face of an old woman, affixed to the lean body and long neck of a lithe young girl. If you'd seen her from behind or at a distance—her head turned away for a moment—you would register *Model. Looker. Beautiful lanky sexy*. But when she'd turn to face you and you confronted her full aspect, shock might assault you. For it is rare to see an old face on such a lilting, long young body. Mary could not be called beautiful.

In carriage and stature she was startling, hypnotic.

Once the face came into focus, though, the picture felt urgently, alarmingly wrong.

Why an old face? Elements colluded. Mary's coloring was swarthy; her eyes, though a pleasant greenish-turquoise, were recessed; her nose narrow. As I recall, her skin was rough and pocked; perhaps there'd been a bad childhood pox or later a bout with acne. But the chief disturbance in Mary's face was her mouth. It appeared she'd lost her teeth, for the structure generally lent by teeth to mouth and lips seemed missing; her mouth sank back in her skull like that of a toothless elder. Though in fact her teeth certainly existed they presented as receding, small and mottled. Without doubt the Hamlins had no money for dentists. In any case it was disturbing to come upon Mary straight-on, to face that sunken, slightly manic smile, because—in no small part due to that smile—hers was the terrifying aspect of a madwoman.

I'd not seen her, nor heard her voice, since the beginning of high school.

I came to the phone, heart pounding. Suddenly the house I lived in, all the jobs and travel and lovers, countless stories I'd lived since Sacramento days, seemed made of sand.

I took the receiver and heard Mary's voice.

It sounded the same after all the intervening years—flat, composed, sardonic—but with a sort of insane glee flickering through it and around it, little volts. Someone had told me, along the interim years of erratic communications with old school friends, that Mary had been involved with drugs. That could hardly surprise me. The hour of her call to me in Hawaii would have been a very late hour on the mainland, so I expected she was loaded now.

These were the days of land-lines only. And long-distance bills.

I stood awkwardly by the side table, holding the receiver with two hands. I tried to make my voice bright and interested, as if this were something that happens all the time. Your old best friend phones you after, what, eighteen years.

I tried, with my voice, for a hearty lilt. No doubt it rang taut and squeaky.

Mary? Mary, how *are* you. What's been happening? What's

going on there?

(Where "there" was, of course, I had no clue. I could only assume it was the Hamlin house because none of them could afford to live anywhere else.)

I'm *wonderful*, said the flat manic voice with its queer, glib irony, giggling. The giggle terrified me. A silence behind her voice— so still—stillness that smothered; a dead sound. I'm having a *smahhhshing* time, said the voice, affecting a vague English accent. Things couldn't be *peachier*.

Caustic laughter erupted, joining with a man's laughter in the background.

I've got my boyfriend here, Mary said. We thought we'd find you. Track you down. My old best friend.

More laughter—hers and his—awful, gloating.

They were surely flying—on what, I could only guess.

As I spoke, I tried to understand how Mary had located my Hawaii phone number, which was unlisted. She must have called my stepmother (my father dead by then), and my stepmother, always disgusted by the pointlessness of my zigzagging life, gave out my number with annoyance; for her, a fruitless chore. I realized I had no idea what to say to Mary and felt panic lumping at the back of my throat. A massive, loaded sarcasm soaked her tone, the aggressive kind that drunks often mount, that feeds viciously on earnestness (and makes the earnest responder feel and sound like a worse fool in her own ears). Suddenly terrified, I dreaded revealing a single specific of my whereabouts, lest Mary and her friend try to fly over and find me.

Later I would feel sharply ashamed of this. (But I couldn't rescind the fear.)

I could have *encouraged* Mary to find me. I could have offered to visit her. I could have tried to find out what, exactly, was happening to her.

I could have tried to affect the direction of things. Had some influence.

But those would have been the efforts of a woman confidently in charge of her life.

At the time I had no resources, no idea of a future. I was paying rent to sleep on a couch in a household of two not-too-stable women, navigating their exes and lovers and cocaine habits and unhappy children. I was girding to fly back to the Bay Area and restart from scratch.

Mary's boyfriend took the receiver.

I now think, piecing it together from things Reeve later told me, that the boyfriend was called Benny. His voice sounded gliding and smooth—wry, stoned. Later in life such a voice would only be too recognizable: that of a buzzed con man, an articulate casualty. I pictured the two of them performing acrobatic sexual feats while blindingly high. Worse, I sensed some ghastly fatalism feeding this downspiral, urging it along: *We've nothing else* (I imagined their reasoning), *no past no future; might as well cash in whatever chips.* Like all drunks or junkies, they were certain of only this single, delirious moment. Meaning would soon abandon them, drop them screaming like a bundle of refuse from a plane's hold—until or unless they could scrabble up the means to get high again.

I've no idea what I said to Benny. He sounded much older than Mary, which further unnerved me. I wonder now whether that man is alive or dead—and if he lives, whether he remembers Mary, or the phone call of that night. Whether he has the remotest idea what happened to the extravagant, long-limbed creature he'd stumbled into, like some sauntering Mardi Gras parade-float goddess.

Staring sightlessly at the suburban wallpaper before me, I must have stuttered out some ridiculous pleasantry about Mary. Maybe I asked were they having a good time—absurd noises. I do remember his comment—across all these years—its proprietary slam-dunk, thick with smug ownership, with self-satisfaction. To this hour his words make something seize in my chest.

She's sublime, the unknown man said.

Some few years later, I learned, somehow, that Mary was dead. The implication and assumption, from whichever high school acquaintance passed the fact to me, seemed to be that death had probably been due to an overdose. I can no longer guess who offered the information, or how authoritatively the informer may have figured in my perception. But in a peculiar response to this— one I can't immediately account for—I stuffed away the knowledge as if slamming shut an untidy drawer, unable or unwilling for years to sort its contents. Since I had as yet no hard context to which to attach it, it's possible I was telling myself that it had *not* happened; that the end of Mary seemed more rumor than fact.

Return

In the years following my return to California I was swept along fast by the necessary, predictable dramas of rebuilding a mainland life: finding a room to rent, resuming work, making friends, learning my way inside a Bay Area exploding with a technical revolution whose implications no one could yet dream. I soon settled into rounds that came to fit like a pliable slipper, grungy yet softened, comfortably conformed to the shape of the life it sheathes.

I loved the city's saline air, cool fogs and pungent eucalyptus; loved the people moving in a freeflow hodgepodge. Air itself seemed to move more crisply, vibrant with possibility—unlike the soft, humid languor of Hawaii. Though in fact it was only a little over a two-hour drive to the Sacramento suburb where Mary and I had met and come of age, fantasized, fine-tuned our dreams, I lived in a world that felt as different from Sacramento as Mars. I kept that division sealed.

I worked an office job, went to aerobics classes, bought a pair of canaries, played records, walked, wept, dreamed. I fell almost at once into a doomed love affair with a married man—a steady carousel of scenes, sulks, confrontations, tears, drinking, delirious reunions, vows and declarations almost immediately reversed, interleaved with teeth-chattering solitudes. It would take six years to step off this carousel. Strangely or not, the city's calm pearliness, its unthinking daily mists and grit, easily absorbed all drama and dramatic gestures: a perfect backdrop for the tireless pageant of our urgencies, a charming stage set for our ruinous, passionate exertions. Everyone was acting out—fevered control-panel manipulators in our lonely starships. We were fulfilling an agenda. Living hard. Being beautiful. Waking up each morning on that gorgeous fist of land jutting into its salty, windy, fish-smelling bay, its mighty bridges leading out and in: the theater of us endlessly fascinating to us. Those were the years of our thirties, an age which believes the very stars are watching.

We'd not yet grasped they've done so eternally—without

interest, without opinions.

When the thought occasionally surfaced that I should seek out the Hamlins and unearth whatever the actual story of Mary had been, I couldn't seem to find a way to begin. The queer aftertaste of Mary's last phone call still distressed me: so did my guilt at having been frightened and repelled by her—though I pray she never sensed it, which I reasoned to be unlikely, as her own brains had surely been cooking on who knew what kind of flame. Onto this wretched inability to face the past piled still more guilt, for my paranoid horror that she might try to find me, might invade my (puny, marginal) life in Hawaii. It is difficult to dwell long with such shame—maybe with any shame. So I went about my days blocking off the whole history, and begged my conscience to be still.

Back to Before

Here's the part you'll have wanted to know. I can tell you some, but not all.

It's become white noise.

About the father—a warm, humane, handsome, beloved teacher—being unable to resist his young female students. About the many affairs conducted recklessly, desperately, drunkenly. How the college dean, confronted with flagrant photographs of yet another affair (collected by a private detective), fired the father. How the father confessed everything to the mother, swore they would make a new start, and found a new teaching job in Sacramento (references must have agreed to protect him). How, because he would be obliged to begin at the new college straightaway, the father traveled to Sacramento alone, rented the apartment on Winding Way. How the crushed mother acceded; she and their two little girls would join him there, after the school year had ended.

How the two little girls, ages nine and eleven, understood only that their father was away at a new job and that they would join him after the school year ended; the little girls had no reason to regard this arrangement as anything other than a thing that happened. How their mother seemed to grow even quieter and sadder, sitting with her eyes closed at the dining table, a tendril of reluctant blue cigarette smoke spiraling up. But their mother had always been quiet and sad; they didn't know any other kind of mother. How they played all day as summer waned, willful, feckless, together and with neighbor kids; how they made baloney sandwiches and milk with chocolate powder stirred in, hiked the desert hills, drew hopscotch squares in chalk on the sidewalk, ran up and down Vista Bonita Road until the bats came careening around in the teal-blue dusk. How on the morning of Labor Day, just before grade school was to start, they woke and their mother still slept so they watched cartoons and the oldest girl began ironing, feeling virtuous for helping her still-sleeping mother this way. It was a hot clear morning, the roses bright outside the screen door, and the basket of wrinkly shirts quite full; on and on she ironed, spraying the rumpled clothes, breathing the warm-clean smell, liking the rhythmic hiss of hot metal pushing fabric smooth. And then her little sister went to make a bowl of cereal and, finding the box empty, thought their mother might know where more cereal was. How the little sister went to wake their mother and wandered back into the living room to tell her big sister that their mother would not wake up.

Then this part of it goes faster, and smears: how the big sister entered the bedroom and saw her mother lying on her side, blanket loose around her middle, eyes closed. How she said the words *Mom, Mommy, Momma*; ventured closer; noticed her mother's lips were oddly blue, and that the flesh of her face sagged in a not-right way. How she touched her mother's arm: *Mom. Momma. Mommy.* How the armflesh was cool and gave beneath her touch in a wrong way, without springing back. How the big sister knew then, her brain silently shrieking; how she ran from the house to the next door neighbors, ancient Maurice Castle and his even-older mother: *Please come quick something's wrong with my mother.* How the two old people followed at once behind her as she raced back; how Maurice held her beside the bedroom door while his shriveled prim mother who looked like Whistler's mother moved to the bedside. How the big sister did not look to see the expression on the old woman's face when it glanced up. How Maurice Castle suddenly clasped the big sister tightly to his scratchy, camphor-smelling wool vest and stared glazed into the air above her, as if he were confronting an invisible arbiter of some kind just above the girl's head, his wire-rim spectacles glinting white with morning light. How the little sister somehow remembered where to find the piece of paper bearing their father's California phone number. How the father flew home that day and gathered and held both daughters in the big nubbly mauve-colored easy chair that had always been his throne, an arm tightly around each little girl while he cried—the first time she had ever seen her father or any man cry, a kind of crumpled wheezing—and how before he arrived home that day, someone sent the sisters down the street to play with neighbor kids. How no one talked, during those playing hours, about what had just happened, and it seemed like a faraway bad dream. They played Monopoly and Parcheesi and Go Fish.

7

I Made the Call

During those years after my return to the mainland, despite my reflex-wish to erase history, curiosity impelled me to act.

But the results of that action so shocked me, so blindsided me, I tried instantly to forget them—and almost succeeded.

Only latterly does this interval appear, shivering forward, smudgy, as if seen through a dirty aquarium. How many years since that day? That number alone may itself now shock.

It took a long time before this scene surfaced through memory's murk like a piece of stained cork, a bloated shoe.

I phoned Faith Hamlin from my day job, at a front desk in San Francisco.

I was always broke, and the office did not, I reasoned, track phone charges too carefully.

I remember staring out the window at the city skyline, a guileless afternoon. The soft, silver-cloud-filtered light through the double-paned glass of the office window; the susurrant crawl of traffic one story below, must have lulled me into believing my action a bland diversion: a tidying of small, stray bits of past business.

I must have also supposed it a gesture, the polite thing to do.

Checking back in after years away.

Faith remembered me. Her voice was the same, but anguished, diffuse—if anything, crazier. If a voice could wring its hands, over and over, that's what hers was doing.

She called me by my name—not one beat's hesitation. Why do drunks and crazies have the most meticulous memories? Faith sounded druggy with pain. Stretched out on a slow rack, witless with pain. Her voice shredded.

I'm not. Doing—so well. It's very. Hard.

I heard the suffering. Incalculable. A vortex.

Oh, Faith. I'm sorry. I'm so sorry.

I couldn't think what else to say. Stricken, I realized I should never have called. What on earth had I been thinking to undertake such a thing, as if reaching for a can on a grocery shelf? The afternoon went dark around my eyes.

As if sensing my horrified panic, my instant longing to escape, her voice pressed in closer, higher, thinner, insistent, incredulous with pain. Wailing like a dying cat. The way grieving women in other cultures tear at their clothes, strike themselves, pull at their hair.

Faith, Faithie. I'm so sorry, was all I could think to say.

Clive must have been long dead by then.

It's very hard, she said again and again. She began to sob low, coarse sobs.

The steel elevator doors in front of my desk opened; bodies emerged, gliding in different directions. Bodies from other directions entered the elevator. All of them young, handsome, blithe. Central to their own twinkly universes. The steel doors slid shut.

I turned my swivel-seat toward the window, my back to the elevator. I hunched over, a forefinger plugging my free ear.

Faith, I'll come visit you soon, okay? Would that be all right— if I came over? Faithie?

(Lying, a frenzy of extravagant lying.)

She was crying uncontrollably. She was telling me, while she cried, what had happened: unspeakable things. My ears heard them but at the time simply could not receive them, could not take them in.

Okay then, Faith? I'll stop by over there real soon. At the house. Okay? See you soon?

She was sobbing.

Faith. Oh God I'm so sorry, Faith, I'm so sorry.

I hung up.

I watched my hand put the receiver down, staring at it, while she was still wailing.

All color had bled from the day. Around me, gray forms.

I must have walked around the building, gone to pee, taken a drink of water. I must have looked out the window. And then I must have turned with relief to answering the phone, typing, filing. What I'd heard was unbearable.

More Suppressed Information

Someone told me later—somewhere I recall seeing a copy of the actual document—that a coroner's report for Marion listed the cause of her death as a surfeit of barbiturate in her blood, identified as coming from a bottle of sleeping pills prescribed for my father.

My father was tall, manly, strong.

Marion was tiny and frail.

No one told me what was done with her remains.

I wondered where the unclaimed ashes of the dead go, in Phoenix—or anywhere.

Think Again

Too many years ago—so many now that the number will qualify me as archaic—the note arrived in the mail. Hand-printed on one of those small, lined notebook pads, postmarked Nevada, from Tommy Hamlin.

Tommy!

I was then, en route to writing books, making essays for magazines. He had seen an article of mine and written me in care of its publisher. He'd recognized my name and wanted to find me.

My father and mother, and Mary, are dead, Tommy wrote.

Please call. I miss my friends from the past.

I lived in an upstairs apartment in the Sunset District of San Francisco at the time, always cold, always damp. Mail dropped through a slot at the base of the stairs leading up to the apartment from the front door. The stairs were carpeted in horrible multi-colored shag that, no matter how you tried to vacuum it, smelled like an old dog. This was where I stood, the chilly dark base of this stairwell, to examine mail. I pulled the letter from the stack of flyers and advertisements; when I'd opened and read it, I felt stilled for some while.

How should I respond to Tommy?

Unnerved, I postponed. Afraid of what?

I forced myself to write Tommy Hamlin a brief thanks, with a promise to stay in touch. No answer came.

I carried on. Love affairs. Money panic. Job changes.

Then one early spring I drove to my sister in those familiar old Sierras: my little hatchback winding up along Highway 80 between the worn-dinosaur backs caped in diamond-powder snow, blinding in the midday sun. I listened to Paul Simon and

Ladysmith Black Mambazo sing *homeless, homeless, moonlight sleeping on a midnight lake*—and let the past rise to the surface, fat and slow and turning. En route to the scrubby foothills, I passed through Sacramento and its shabby outskirts over the river. Again I spotted those few old houses that used to spook and thrill and mystify me, listing, paintless, splintering out in the midst of their dried-up fields: sightless, curtaining who knew what stories—by now only the filling-in stillness, the progeny of air left behind from those stories. Far fewer such houses stood now, of course, steadily chewed up by repeating conglomerates of strip malls and big-box stores, unfurling fast-forward over the valuable land between the central valley and Bay Area.

Roseville now burgeoning, a commuter suburb.

The old homes evaporating, banished to the ephemerality of memory.

That was when I began to think again about Mary.

Someone had told me, at the same time as they had announced her death, that there was a child.

Mary had borne a daughter.

Sealed Off

Tommy's phone never answered; there was no recording.

Two letters to the address he'd given on his note, went unanswered. I had no other leads.

Faith and Clive were dead. I had no means yet of learning what had become of Lucy.

Finally, I summoned nerve to phone a high-school friend—I'll call her Gemma—who had spent most of her teenage years in the Hamlin house. Gemma was a funny, spirited tomboy who'd mugged her way through school, lost her parents and nearly herself to alcohol, and finally found peace and sobriety after she married and raised her children—now long grown and out in the world. She lives in a small, pretty mining town. Gemma is the sort of woman who nests a home, sees to the comforts of people around her, makes them laugh. She was this way in high school, a kind and easy presence. Her bungalow perches near the banks of the town's clear river, a river moving all year with snowmelt. The train that passes bravely through can still be heard every day, not far from the house.

At first Gemma sounded troubled about my questions. In turn, I felt embarrassed; how crass to be phoning with the purpose of gaining information—I had known where Gemma lived for many years, and with the usual excuses of fatigue and complicated schedules, made no effort to see her. But I was damned glad to speak with her now, to reminisce at first about our own pasts, threading through preliminaries: health, love, children and stepchildren, school chums. Soon we found something like our old conversational rhythm. I pictured her sitting on a blanket-strewn sofa looking out to the river, its lovely clear green.

Gemma spoke of the Hamlins.

For several years she had lived fulltime with them. They had virtually adopted her, she said, after a period when her own life at home had disintegrated.

Faith was in her 50s when Gemma knew them; Clive in his 60s. This came as the first shock: Faith and Clive had both appeared to me, during my visits there, to be at least 15 years older.

Gemma hastily agreed with this: they'd been *like the fragile, dotty elderly*, she said. And their drinking finished off whatever vitality may have remained in them—especially for Clive, she added.

Clive had worked for the Army Corps of Engineers, Gemma told me. But what, I asked, about the newspaper writing? He had done that too, she said. Articles about Corps projects, for the paper. But his career was slowly, then rapidly, poisoned by cheap alcohol and ill health—a causality, she added, in that sequence. In the years she and I knew the Hamlins, Gemma said, Clive perfected the original stereotype (Gemma's words) of the falling-down drunk. Most of the time he stayed, as I'd recalled, up in the bedroom, and from time to time he would yell out from there. But he escaped his upstairs lair more often than I'd known, and this had caused havoc. Sometimes, Gemma said sadly, he wet himself. Sometimes they found him crawling—literally crawling—across the yard's dew-soaked grass at night.

The family tried every way it could to keep Clive from driving, but too often he would somehow manage to find the car keys and take off. It was a miracle, Gemma said with a sigh, that no one was hit. Finally Clive went into the hospital, and one thing rapidly led to the inevitable. His official cause of death was listed as bacterial infection but it was in fact, Gemma told me ruefully, more a kind of "pile-up" of all that had happened, that did him in.

Reeve, the eldest and—on its surface—perhaps the sanest of the lot, was away a great deal, she said, in Berkeley, where he'd become a painter and builder; much later, he moved to the Sierra foothills. Reeve's stance toward the family's decomposition seemed—to Gemma in those days—to be distant and disdainful, doing his best to ignore what could never be repaired. Tommy, however—according to Gemma—*still carries the sadness in him*. He languishes, was the way Gemma put it—that is, she said, the sadness never quite leaves him. (Here Gemma paused a quiet beat.) He is still so handsome, she went on, that people in shops stop talking when he enters. They go silent, staring at him, and they don't resume their talk or business until he leaves. Tommy works, she said, as a fire-spotter in the mountains during summer, and in winter as an avalanche blaster and snowplough operator—away from most people most of the time.

In the years of high school, after Mary and I drifted apart, Gemma spent almost all her time away from school, in the Hamlin house. She shopped and cooked with them, drank and smoked with them, kept the huge Dripolator coffeepot filled with fresh brew from the big, yellow-labeled cans of generic grounds the family bought. She looked things up in the outdated Brittanica encyclopedia set the Hamlins kept near the dining nook, and—continually drinking coffee or jug wine—argued politics and ethics with them late into the night.

We didn't know what we were talking about most of the time, she admitted cheerfully.

But we had, Gemma said—after a pause—*a feeling for each other*. Her voice tightened.

It was a world, she said. For better and for worse. Sealed off.

Gemma spoke frankly about her long love affair, during those years, with Tommy.   As everyone within sight of him at any moment knew, Tommy Hamlin presented as a bewilderingly handsome, yet utterly natural and genuine, young man; his manner always unselfconscious, shambling, amiable. Like a young James Taylor, Gemma said calmly, as if reciting statistics. (In a way, I supposed, she was.) Though she was a few years older than Tommy, Gemma must have shared with him a sibling-like coziness in that strange, curtained-off shelter from the chaotic world, on Juniper Street. They remain good friends today, she said, and Tommy still loves to travel.

Another pause.

Did I remember, Gemma asked, the time Tommy and Reeve went hitchhiking across the country? (This sounded a faint bell, but was buried so deeply there was no sense wasting time trying to dredge it up.)

Please remind me, I said.

I could hear her fondness. The brothers, she said, had loved embarking on every kind of adventure.

(But so had Mary and I! So had we!)

They'd be gone for months, she went on. This trek took them across the whole continent and back.

Where they had gone, what they had done, whom and what they had seen—all this seemed immaterial in Gemma's telling. What was most important about it was that Gemma had known *instinctively*, she said—her voice warming—without anyone alerting her by letter or by phone, the absolute exact day and even *hour* that Reeve and Tommy would return. She was waiting with the rest of the family in the kitchen. (She had alerted them all, in a hysterical sweep of the building and grounds, that the boys' homecoming was upon them.) When the feeling that they were very near overpowered her, she said, she banged out the screen door onto the sloping front yard, shooing away the incensed, flapping Gus— the bird knew her after all her time there—her heart pounding and her eyes wet and wide with looking.

And sure enough: there around the bend onto Juniper Street they loped, two lean brown brothers long-striding it in the afternoon sun, their dark hair and jeans and packs and duffels, straight brown hair falling into their eyes: Reeve's robin's-egg-blue and Tommy's dark chocolate ones—grinning their daredevil RAF grin.

My God, Gemma breathed to me.

The sight of the two of them. You remember how they *looked?* she asked.

Oh, I remembered.

We sat a moment with this.

I know that Gemma's own blond, Buster Brown-cut hair is pure white now. And my brunette mane—once down-my-back, phone-book-thick—is tinted its present brown, cropped to a curly cap.

Both of us have faces you might very politely call *etched*.

Faith died twenty years ago, Gemma said, sighing once more.

It seemed as if all the things that had happened *took pieces of her away*, Gemma said. Faith had been, by the end, very ill with cancer. Toward the last, Tommy went to take care of her.

Oh, Tommy. What did you hear? What did you see?

So Little for So Long

Gemma had to be the one to tell me, during our first conversation on the phone, when I asked how it happened.

Her voice grew tighter still: pain, exasperation, terrible sadness. Her words came in a series of hapless blurts.

Mary committed suicide, she said.

A beat.

My God, I murmured. How?

(Why do we always ask that?)

Gemma's voice rose because there was no way around the information: it became a keening, control momentarily lost.

She hanged herself—near Faithie's back steps, on a swing, using the swing's rope.

The picture came instantly to me.

I saw a blackened face and coated eyes and that slow, gentle twisting—perhaps a final remnant of an expression, perhaps around the mouth: a voided satisfaction, a sly triumph. And I heard Faith's eventual screams—cannot think how Faith lived on another moment, in any form, after that sight.

Gemma spoke quickly but with conviction. Her voice held a kind of wrought acceptance that a listener knows has taken a great deal of time to achieve.

It was, she told me more quietly, the ultimate tragedy of the Hamlins.

Because their tragedies were many. Because they were—toward the last—so out of control they could not take care of each other.

Faith and Clive, Gemma said very slowly—as if reprising the lines of a grieving nursery rhyme—*here is the church, here is the steeple*—Faith and Clive were older parents overwhelmed by four wily, willful children.

They were also running out of money, and Clive was falling apart.

The Hamlins were always resisting this downslide, Gemma said. I think the sixties did them no service, she added—terrible things going on inside families, but no one speaking about them. Everyone keeping their awful secrets, in secret shame. And the family had been striving to live on so little, she said, for so long.

But I remember we always ate so fabulously, so heartily, I said.

How did that happen?

Because, answered Gemma (with patience, as if expecting the question), Faith was a crackerjack bargain shopper. She bought generic groceries; knew how to stretch a dollar—almost impossibly well. Still, there was never enough. Mary and her baby daughter Sara lived in a little house out back for a time. Don't you remember, Gemma suddenly pleaded, the year Mary tried to stage a sit-down strike at the Governor's office, for being denied a job at the Greyhound bus station? No one took her seriously; everyone just figured she was crazy.

No, I couldn't remember that. I must have been in Hawaii. But the act rang consistent, in some awful way, with the delusional convictions that must always have been components—or habits— of Mary's mind, that burst into ghoulish bloom under pressures of no money and no prospects and probably, public scorn: rejections of various grab-bag schemes and decisions frantically, histrionically devised: *try this; try that.*

I wound back the film, and saw Mary's mind snap cleanly at some desperate, determinate moment.

Say she was trying—yet another botched attempt—to buy something, paints, or bananas, or aspirin. Perhaps she was burning under yet another series of contemptuous stares and scornful comments from salesclerks when her wallet could not produce the required bills and coins. Perhaps she had pushed too long, without response or effect, to get ahead of moneylessness; fought too often, loudly, cruelly, with her mother; been forced to cadge pocket change yet again from Faith or from her brothers, wretchedly, for some small need; been repelled one too many times by locked faces of receptionists and secretaries, social service workers and employment agency matrons who told her coldly they were *really very sorry there was nothing they could do.*

Indifference and hostility and cold refusal, wherever she turned.

They're all against me, against me, against me, I heard her mind humming.

And I could easily imagine that hum building on itself like compounding swarms of bees, the multiplied buzz escalating to a roar as her solution began to dawn, slowly at first and then brilliantly, racing. Faith might have been napping, or at the grocery store; the boys away on one of their junkets; Clive insensible upstairs. Perhaps there was also medication that Mary'd ceased to take, or that she'd taken too much of. But where was little girl, Sara? Ah, yes: with her father, in her father's house. The child would be cared for now (Mary would have told herself); ample family remaining would care for her, yes. Mary's mind would have been talking to itself freely this way, faster and faster, telling stories, prescribing, supposing, proposing: step by step, almost singing to herself as she complied, went about assembling the ingredients. The swing. A way to loop the swing-rope onto itself, large enough to fit over the head. Looping. Again. Heart shirring, shirring. Remembering how they do it: someplace she saw it, a movie, a photograph; wherever she last saw how they do it. Will that hold? Her thoughts like bees. Maybe the sun warmed her, full of motes from wildflowers. Maybe a night breeze, young grass blades pressed like piano keys. Maybe the dark cloaked her frantic motions, accelerating for the vast, velvet certainty of relief, of solving everything in a smooth, sweet sweep: certainty swirling and fluttering down like silken petals, enclosing her, petting her, like soft snow petting her, quilting the scene, all the sharp edges coated and rounded. Finally, purpose was clear. Direct. Pure. Busy. *This will take care of things.* Eliminate all pain, convey the exact message. The dusk, the mote-filled light, the empty lumpy yard; the dull whoosh of passing cars, screech of a jay claiming territory, clicking of waking crickets, dog's distant bark; patterns in fading light—all of it must have at last sung in exaltation with her; celestial chorus urging her melting, spinning mind.

Mary's funeral, Gemma said, was an open casket service.

I could not make myself go near it, she said.

All I could see from a distance, Gemma said, was the tip of her nose.

8

Reeve

The way parachutists freefall, one by one from unseen dimensions of sky, aiming so they come together in a hand-held circle that continues, at unthinkable speeds, to fall—holding off deploying their chutes for as long as they dare—so have these isolated pieces of the story of Mary begun to fall toward a single remembering, each clasping on to the next as it appears.

I reached Reeve Hamlin by phone, not long after talking with Gemma. It had been, easily, thirty-five years.

He was relaxed, calm, his voice exactly the same. He remembered me clearly.

He was married. A painter. After years in Berkeley as a landscape architect he traveled, and now paints fulltime:

"For me—and for Mary," he said.

He painted her a mural, he said, on a long, public wall in the rural, norther-western town where he now lives.

Reeve! That confident, wry tone—so western, I now reflected; just as it had been long ago: same droll amusement I'd painfully swooned for as a youngster. Only the timbre of his voice betrayed the meddling of time—grainier with age.

Reeve did not hesitate to talk about his family. He began at once.

Faith and Clive Hamlin met in Minnesota, he told me, at a dance. Clive had just graduated in journalism from a nearby university. Eric Sevareid was his classmate, Reed said. Faith, who'd fled North Dakota, was attending a teacher's college in the small Minnesota town where her school held the dance.

They determined to make a life together. Clive obtained work with the Civilian Conservation Corps, which brought them to California. Eventually Clive bought land north of Sacramento in the Folsom hills, where the couple lived in a cabin without plumbing or electricity, while Clive drove all the way to downtown Sacramento each day to write his reports for the Army Corps of Engineers—also to appear in the *Bee*. Reeve was three at the time of the move out west. Eventually they built the house on Juniper Street, and proceeded to bring into being the rest of their children.

Reeve seemed to be voting, as he spoke, for his father. "He's where all the talent came from," he said.

I surmised that Reeve had been closest to Clive, perhaps even compelled to take up his father's case against the others' attacks. Faith had been an educated woman—I remember her following the daily papers, being distressed by inhumane news. This was also borne out by Gemma's accounts of the family's arguing current affairs into the night. If, in the final third of her life, Faith acted and sounded addled, I'd still assumed her to be informed and thoughtful, straitjacketed by the duties of family. But Reeve, it appeared, had had little patience with his mother, or much sympathy for her. Whatever made her what she was—or became—seemed to have occurred so far back, Reeve himself might never be able to know. I thought of Levertov's famous line: *The myriad past / It enters us, and disappears.*

And of Mary?

Reeve kept his declarations mild. Her relationships "never panned out," he said quietly. The man she conceived baby Sara with—she had known, Reeve said, that she wanted a baby, and Mary would get what she wanted—this man was not to Reeve's liking: "something of a lightweight." (I sensed all Reeve's words to be almost wildly understated.) Mary tried, he said, to finish school; the family had wanted this for her. She attended several colleges in several counties, and finally managed to graduate with a bachelor's degree in art. (She had also, it seemed, stuffed away a lot of dunning notices—demands for repayment of loans, which Reeve unearthed among her things after it was all over.) But Mary found after graduation that it was nearly impossible get a job in art, or anything remotely to do with art. She did hold occasional shows of her work—but she maintained "an attitude," as Reeve put it, that pushed people away.

"She hurt people," he said simply.

Though she had never hurt me, I could imagine Mary applying sarcasm with hurtful effect. I could imagine it as a formulated defense against fools and idiots.

How had Mary's art changed, I wondered, from the days of the sparkling head-portraits of women?

She kept doing those, Reeve answered. Thousands of them. He still had many of them, of her papers and letters and preliminary studies, whatever he could gather from the Hamlin house after Mary died. There were pages and pages of quick line drawings, he told me, portrait sketches.

But Reeve wanted to say more about the progress of her life.

She had lots of affairs "when she was going crazy," he said— the words *going crazy* were uttered without hesitation. A lot of those affairs had seemed, to him, almost platonic. Meantime, Mary's ex fought her hard for their daughter, and she lost custody of Sara.

She died in September of '84, Reeve said. Sara was five, living with her father.

After Sara's father successfully won custody of the child, Mary had taken up with "a one-eyed, bald, black man" named Benny. (Was it Benny, gloating beside her, when Mary phoned me?) The two lived with Reeve at first. Then they married, and Benny took Mary back to his native Tennessee, where Mary painted and wrote Reeve long letters.

Reeve did not answer these.

For this neglect, he still carries guilt.

"I don't know why I didn't," he said.

His voice tightened, and I could at last hear the current of pain in his mild recital.

His guilt compounded. On return from Tennessee, Mary brought four new paintings to show him. She unrolled them on the floor of the Hamlin house on Juniper Street.

They were, said Reeve, astonishing.

She had broken through her former limits, he said, crossed the threshold. Her new work was after the manner, he said, of four supreme painters: Van Gogh, Gauguin—she had loved Gauguin, he told me—Picasso, and Cezanne. Reeve loved her new paintings, and he is sure he told Mary they were good—but now accuses himself of not having been emphatic enough.

"I didn't give her enough pats," he said, helplessly.

And I began to grasp that Reeve had held a great deal of power, whether or not he'd chosen to wield it, as the eldest of the four Hamlin children, his father's most trusted friend, a successful working artist and perhaps, also, a sane and loving father-substitute to his siblings. It would only follow. His younger sisters and brother would have looked to him for approval, protection, affection. That his choosing to give or withhold any portion of these *was* his power. Reeve's blessing would have eased and exonerated, his affirmation fixed wholeness and meaning. And his disapproval, or even lack of response, would have made the ground unsteadier beneath them.

It was not clear to me that Reeve had ever been generous with his responses.

But he had let Mary and Benny live with him a while, he said. And after Mary died, when fourteen-year-old Tommy was "having trouble," Reeve took him in.

Mary had broken through her limits and become very good at her art, Reeve said. Yet this had not helped her at all as she looked about for paying work: her talent hadn't made anyone more willing to help her. Her fine paintings made not one bit of difference. No jobs were forthcoming, no commissions. Mary had to find some way to earn a living.

She offered to throw pots for Reeve's landscaping business. What she immediately produced, he said, was of superb quality, "almost too good" for his straightlaced clientele. She thought she might try to teach art therapy, but no openings materialized. She wound up, Reeve said, taking "the most godawful jobs." Cleaning up after old people, he said. Night clerking at convenience stores and flophouses in the worst parts of town. I remembered Gemma's descriptions of Mary trying to stage a sit-down strike outside the governor's office, because she had been denied a job at a Greyhound bus station. Such a tactic, to me, hinted of creeping madness, some terrible, momentum-gathering spiral of prophecy fulfillment.

"I think," Reeve said, sounding sadder and sadder, "she took the horrible jobs to punish herself in some way.

"She got religion more or less about then," he said. He asked whether I remembered P., a neighborhood girlfriend. (I did, vaguely.) She and Mary began spending time together in churches, Reeve said—a lot of time.

Sara had been living with her father for less than a year. The father had fought for custody of the child, Reeve said, mainly to oppose Mary: he knew Mary wanted her. But Reeve also admitted in the next breath that Mary might not have been good for her little daughter. Sometimes, he'd noticed, she was tense and impatient with the little girl, brushing her daughter's hair too hard, punitively.

He also knew that Mary "was running around carrying knives."

Reeve suggested to Mary that it was not good to be doing such things.

But—these were his words—a person "never knew what rational was, with Mary," he said.

Mary began to believe she had been singled out for difficulty, for bad treatment, Reeve said. She felt that Faith was angry with her more than with any of the others; that everyone was turning against her, trying to make her life harder. She began wanting, in retaliation, "to ruin everybody's life," Reeve said. Marijuana made things worse, Reeve added. "It put her into a crazy space right away." There was a swing in front outside the Hamlin kitchen, which hung from a large amount of rope. One evening when he was visiting and they passed it together, Mary glanced at the swing and remarked slyly to him that there was enough rope there to *take care of herself.* Reeve quoted this phrase to me. He had looked hard at his sister immediately and said, you wouldn't do that. She was passing it off then, he said, as a joke. But now, Reeve told me, he can see that in fact "she was working up to it," even though they'd had a perfectly good day just the day before she died.

She was living at home with her parents, after a falling-out with Benny.

She must have also had a fight with Faith that day. Or perhaps she'd just quietly come to the end of her resistance in the silence of afternoon.

And even though she'd tied herself inside the fatal knot, using the swing's rope—I will spend the rest of my life wondering at this—*she did not use a chair.*

She just sat down on the swing. She was not high up off the ground.

She could have stood up at any time, said Reeve.

That's what stops me. Again and again.

Worst: Mary made sure, Reeve said, to die in a place that she knew would be the *first thing her mother would see* when she looked out the kitchen window.

The night it happened, Reeve had fallen asleep in front of the television at his own home. He had seen his sister the day before.

The phone rang at 2:00 a.m., waking him. He opened his eyes to white noise and a speckled grainy pattern on the television screen. The caller was the county sheriff, who told him his sister was hanging outside her parents' house. He slammed out of the house to jump into the car and race over to Juniper Street.

Reeve told me he was "still angry with the cops," meaning, I guess, for their blustery officiousness.

There were twenty police cars surrounding the Hamlin home when he got there. It must have been blinding for the flashing lights.

Faith had slept through all of it.

Clive was still alive then, though completely bedridden.

When Faith rose next morning, it was all finished. She began wailing: *It should have been me*, feeling she had tipped the balance of Mary's mind the previous day by having told Mary that she, Faith, had wanted to run in front of the cars that passed in front of the Juniper Street house.

It should have been me, she howled over and over.

Clive was not moved by Mary's death, Reeve said.
Why not, I asked.
She tried to kill me, Clive had claimed to Reeve.
How, I asked Reeve. Which of course, he had asked Clive.

By "pushing all the buttons," Reeve said Clive had answered. Saying things she hoped would give Clive a heart attack, shock him to death. Reeve told me all this in a voice that did not waver. Its sadness was the kind, like Gemma's, that has had to settle over many years, having exhausted its earlier, more fiery torments.

And I believed that all these events had migrated, for Reeve, into that realm that becomes part of the long history, the tapestry of all of us—not just that of a single family living out its tortured life in the middle of a century. Another fixture, over time; a background—one painting of so many, on the cave wall.

Lucy

Mary had had a daughter, Gemma told me, a child (no longer now a child). I am calling her Sara.

Gemma said the young woman is well, reared by her father and by Mary's younger sister Lucy, who is now apparently a late-midlife woman with other grown adult children.

I called directory assistance for the city Gemma named, and felt my skin tighten as I heard on the answering machine recording, after thirty-odd years, baby sister Lucy's voice: now an aging woman's, logical, modulated, toughened at its edges, announcing the names of various grown children and where they might be reached. What fluttered in my ear was a slight redolence of Mary's voice—too loud, as if the extra volume were intended as bravado but cranked a shade too hard, so that the listener suspected (in whatever portion of brain assesses this) a component of carefully repressed hysteria.

I left some sort of stumbling message, wondering how, if she called back, to begin.

Lucy never returned my call.

No message is a clear message. I had no heart to pursue it.

All We Know

I came back to the Phoenix house, once, with my sister and her two young sons.

Vista Bonita had been dully retitled: North Second Drive. I have written of it elsewhere, in memoir form, a part of the writer's endless quest to exorcize, to excavate.

Bravely we drove. Bravely we stared at the house, parked across the street, through the glinting afternoon—a house now scarcely recognizable. Two palm trees that had stood like sentries at the front corners of the lawn were long ago removed: even the butts of their trunks had been razed or dug out. What had been lawn was now gravel. Heat stopped the air. Old plastic toys were scattered outside, scratched and simmering in the glare. Of the house itself we could scarcely make out the lines and borders once known so indelibly to us that imagining any other house anywhere always took the shape of this house.

We exited the car and marched to the door (the porch no longer existed; no trace of the trellis with its proud burden of rose vines).

The front door. Our front door. Same door? Surely not. Too fresh. We knocked.

A Caucasian man answered. He looked disheveled. T-shirt, shorts, hair askew. The cool breath from within that came at us was of cooking, the kind you smell in houses with children. Rice? Eggs? Oatmeal or macaroni?

He was a harried father.

My sister explained, breathless. We'd lived here once. Might we be able to have a quick look around inside our once-home.

I stood numb beside her, unable to speak. My brain felt cancelled in a barrage of static.

The man said Yes, but without feeling. He opened the door and stepped back, gesturing us in.

We crept forward into the milk-smelling coolness, like the two little girls we'd once been.

My sister never stopped talking. It was something she did, especially when she was nervous. While she talked I moved about like a sleepwalker, staring at the family's mess, seeing but not quite seeing: a queer sense of my own torso and limbs dissolving as I tried to fix memory over the surfaces before us—in that corner the Hoffman television with its thick yellow screen; against this wall the big Magnavox with the bright-chartreuse vertical line that moved sideways when you turned the tuning knob; here was where our couch had been, where they took the photo of toddling sisters standing on it together; another corner had contained the small, folding, butterscotch formica table where we ate—the way you'd align an old-fashioned photo negative's transparency over a color image. My sister's little boys stood aside, patient, awkward, bored. My head felt crammed with sticky fog. And the droning in my head, a massive bee swarm's, grew louder and louder as I approached the bedroom that had been our parents'. Our mother had slept alone there so much of the time.

Labor Day, late morning, 1961. Our mother apparently still sleeping. Our father gone, beginning the new job in California. Cartoons on television. I am ironing, something I feel proud to do for the family. My sister, age 9, cannot find any cereal, and goes to wake our mother to ask her where more might be kept. She returns, confused, into the living room where I stood ironing, saying our mother will not wake up. I rest the iron and go into the bedroom and she is lying on her side; her face seems to sag very slightly toward the pillow: her lips, unforgettably, a darkish blue.

I touch her arm. *Mom. Mommy. Momma, wake up.*

The arm's flesh, coolish, gives softly; the stilled form makes no response.

Wrong. Wrong wrong wrong. My heart feels as if it has been slugged or mashed, wheezing. I am eleven years old. I race from the room out the door to the next-door neighbors: old Maurice Castle, who lives with his even-older mother. Bang bang bang on their screen door. Tall Mr. Castle appears through the mesh of the screen, his coke-bottle specs magnifying his alarm. *Please Mr. Castle can you come quick there's something wrong with my mother.* Without waiting for a reply I turn and run back to my house. Maurice Castle and his mother come running straight out behind me (I hear their screen door bang): into my own house we stride. I lead them to the bedroom. Mrs. Castle ventures in while Mr. Castle stands beside me outside the doorway to the room, his hand on my shoulder, gently staying me. Then at some signal from the old woman—later I guessed her hands had lifted in surrender like a bank teller's, her head perhaps shaking *no*, her eyes alight with horror—poor Maurice Castle's face goes taut and pale and glassy and without any words he clasps me tightly to his scratchy-vested, camphor-smelling chest.

That's the room I come toward now, without will.

The door is closed.

Without asking permission I open it, my sister's voice cascading in the background.

Inside, alongside an empty bed, is a crib. In the crib, a baby sleeps.

I stare. The blankets around the sleeping infant are loudly colored and pilly; the light muted by curtains. The room smells yeasty with sleep; of baby powder and old milk.

Soft silence, like the afternoon light.

I stare another moment. I back out, close the door. I stand still a while.

We look at other rooms and make our expressions of thanks to the young father and exit the house and drive back to wherever we are staying.

I think a long time about what I have seen.

That it is possible for a baby to be sleeping where someone has died, where death has ended other possibilities—rerouted them.

New life can continue to gather itself, with normal ravenous fury, in the space where prior life stopped. The space makes no objection—exudes no residual poison. Casts no hexing spell.

It is possible.

The second visit happens with my husband, many years later.

My sister is dead. Her sons are grown men rearing families of their own.

I pull the car to the far side of the street, opposite the house. There it squats, nondistinct, a miniscule ugly cementy tract home, flat-faced pill in a vial of hundreds like it, surrounding it in an oppressed, dusty, scrabble-ass neighborhood.

My husband waits, wordless, in the passenger seat beside me.

I don't need to go into the house this time. I bury my face against the steering wheel, and sob.

A barbiturate was found in Marion's system during the autopsy, matching a prescription issued for my father. It was never made clear whether the amount ingested was deliberate, or whether the dose taken had simply overwhelmed a tiny, weakened system.

It is possible your mother just wanted some sleep.

Stone, Like Thee

In winter there is but one weather in Paris, a bloodless, saturating Siberian cold that seeps up through the sidewalk cement straight into your shoes and bones. There is no comfort. Yet the body, hunched and pained and driven—*move, move through it quickly*—is still somehow vitalized, quickened by the forced motion and passion of that dour, supreme city. Breathing diesel fumes and steams of meaty sauces, of pastries and brioches and fresh baguettes, of crepes spread with ham and cheese or chocolate and bananas, of dirty Seine-water and mud-strength coffee: belief survives.

We tried to move faster, to keep warm.

My husband and I stamped across the bridge through misting cold, through fat lacy flakes floating across the gray square, a few bold pigeons flapping at the feet of local benefactors. We paused to gaze up at the tremendous façade, an unopposable face of reckoning, its crowning rows of saints and martyrs staring off past us into rarer realms. At the great edifice's uppermost corners crouched the blackening gargoyles, creatures of pointy ears and fangs, horns and hooves and arrow-tipped tails, petrified in eternal vigil. Their indifference to human pain always confused me; their expressions wry. I heard again Charles Laughton's Quasimodo despairing to one of them:

Why was I not made of stone, like thee!

And who among us, I wonder, has not—at some burning-ruins interval—been Quasimodo?

We waited in long lines to pass through the doors of that ancient, freezing monolith.

At first it feels like entering a towering, above-ground crypt. Icy blackness and murmuring, smell of damp stone, echoes upon echoes, continuous pour of low voices punctuated by a child's cry or shout. Our eyes slowly made out the forms and movement in that bleak vastness: fields of flickering votive flames, herds of humans treading the worn rounds, air stale with old wax and centuries of sorrow. Tourists, even momentarily cowed, are tourists, determined to take possession of what they see: their steady *passeggiata*, their murmurs and exclamations and sharp commands, a river of noise. We moved past the friezes, the life-sized dioramas set in shell-shaped pockets of the carved walls, the giant supporting columns, craning as we walked to look up up up and around in the semi-dark. Treading the ages-old loop: statuary posed in pure surrender to the will of the highest authority; banks of red-wax candles glittering (each red puck lit from within by a flickering-gold heart) surrounded by more pompous reds and golds of ornate, elaborate tapestries. I took measured steps among the milling others. I did not kneel or light a candle, did not curtsy or genuflect, did not lower my head or close my eyes. I held no faith; those habits were an alien language I'd never wished to learn. It seemed unwise to pray in a language not your own.

All of it so stunningly cold. A preview. *The grave's a fine and private place.*

You go ahead, I told my patient husband, who was stamping from foot to foot, muffler masking his lower face and nose like a bandit, hands deep in pockets. We could see the white vapor of our breath.

I'll catch up, I said.

At the completion of the horseshoe-shaped passage I stood a little distance from the pews in that strange, enormity of ancient air, of stale wax and frozen stone and reverberating voices. It could have been some cosmic bus station. A few determined souls huddled along the rows of seats, heads buried in their folded arms or mashed against clasped hands, necklines and shoulders hunched in meditation or despair, or maybe simply to keep warmer than it was outside, under the lordly dome of this deep old tomb. I stood a few paces from the empty rows of black, hard wood pews nearest the door, the two rows you find just after the entrance.

And wished then, against my scolding, rational instincts, for Mary to at least be allowed to glimpse me there—the Mary I knew before the drowning tides of adulthood. The growing-up girl who'd walked and talked with me on invented adventure— before corrosion, before entrapment, before sex, before lost lonely want isolated her in a sea of conventionality, before hunger and adamant, ignorant enemies, before madness. Let the younger Mary visit this setting now, magically certain and magically protected by that certainty, if only for this moment. That girl. Who'd loved me the way she'd loved everything else then: without reserve, for the joy of being. Pretty ballerina who'd once lived only for being— with soaring, generous, merry expectation.

People would love us.

And when I waken on that dreary Sunday morning,

I open up my eyes to find there's rain,

And something strange within says go ahead and find her,

Just close your eyes . . . yeah. Just close you're your eyes

And she'll be there.

She'll be there.

She'll be there.

Mary, I whispered.

Mary.

About the Author

Joan Frank is the author of twelve books of literary fiction and nonfiction. Her most recent novel, THE OUTLOOK FOR EARTHLINGS, was a ForeWord Reviews book of the month. Her novella collection, WHERE YOU'RE ALL GOING, won the Mary McCarthy Prize for Short Fiction and the gold Independent Publishers Book Award for Literary Fiction. Her collected travel essays, TRY TO GET LOST, won the River Teeth Literary Nonfiction Book Prize. Pending is a new collection of essays, LATE WORK: A LITERARY AUTOBIOGRAPHY OF LOVE, LOSS, AND WHAT I WAS READING. A MacDowell Fellow and recipient of many honors, Joan also reviews literary fiction and nonfiction for the Washington Post, Boston Globe, and similar venues. She lives in California's North Bay Area. Learn more about the author at joanfrank.org

C&R PRESS TITLES

NONFICTION

This is Infertility by Kirsten McLennan
Currciulm Viate by Gregory de la Haba
East Village Closed by Billy the Artist
Many Paths by Bruce McEver
By the Bridge or By the River? Stories of Immigration
from the Southern Border by Amy C. Roma
Women in the Literary Landscape by Doris Weatherford, et al
Credo: An Anthology of Manifestos & Sourcebook for Creative
Writing by Rita Banerjee and Diana Norma Szokolyai

FICTION

Juniper Street by Joan Frank
Transcendent Gardening by Ed Falco
All I Should Not Tell by Brian Leung
Last Tower to Heaven by Jacob Paul
History of the Cat in Nine Chapters or Less by Anis Shivani
No Good, Very Bad Asian by Lelund Cheuk
Surrendering Appomattox by Jacob M. Appel
Made by Mary by Laura Catherine Brown
Ivy vs. Dogg by Brian Leung
While You Were Gone by Sybil Baker
Cloud Diary by Steve Mitchell
Spectrum by Martin Ott
That Man in Our Lives by Xu Xi

SHORT FICTION

A Mother's Tale & Other Stories by Kahanh Ha
Fathers of Cambodian Time-Travel Science by Bradley Bazzle
Two Californias by Robert Glick
Notes From the Mother Tongue by An Tran
The Protester Has Been Released by Janet Sarbanes